selected topics in biology

ANIMAL
BEHAVIOUR

A. P. Brookfield   B.Sc.
Head of Sixth Form Biology
Birkenhead High School G.P.D.S.T.

General Editor
M. B. V. Roberts M.A. Ph.D.

Thomas Nelson and Sons Ltd
Nelson House   Mayfield Road
Walton-on-Thames   Surrey KT12 5PL

P.O. Box 18123   Nairobi   Kenya

Yi Xiu Factory Building
Unit 05–06   5 Floor
65 Sims Avenue   Singapore 1438

Thomas Nelson (Hong Kong) Ltd
Watson Estate   Block A   13 Floor
Watson Road   Causeway Bay   Hong Kong

Thomas Nelson (Nigeria) Ltd
8 Ilupeju Bypass   PMB 21303   Ikeja   Lagos

© A. P. Brookfield 1980
First published 1980
Reprinted 1982, 1983
ISBN 0-17-448086-5
NCN 210-3203-2

Illustrated by:
Brian Denyer
John Hutchinson
David Pratts

Printed and bound in Hong Kong
Phototypeset in Great Britain by
Filmtype Services Limited, Scarborough

General Editor's Preface

The books in this series are written specifically for A-level students who wish to pursue certain areas of biology in depth. We hope the books will be particularly useful to those who are taking special papers or entrance examinations to Oxford or Cambridge.

The writers of books of this kind face a dilemma. On the one hand they want to provide plenty of material to challenge the keen Sixth Former. On the other hand they do not want to smother the poor student with a plethora of detail which he or she will shortly meet again at university. The aim of this series is to broaden the student's view of biology without trespassing on university territory. The emphasis is on providing a wide range of interesting examples and studies which we hope will stimulate thought and enquiry. At the same time we hope that the books will prove enjoyable as well as informative.

In preparing the series we have been highly selective in our choice of topics. We have confined ourselves to those topics which are difficult to cover adequately in a basic textbook and for which we consider there is a need for appropriate books at the Sixth Form level.

Pat Brookfield's book, the first in the series, provides an insight into some of the current issues in animal behaviour and their human implications. She emphasises the neuro-sensory basis of behaviour and thereby brings together the traditionally separate fields of ethology and physiology.

M.B.V. Roberts

Authors' Preface

This book is intended to introduce Sixth formers to some aspects of animal behaviour which cannot be covered in their general text books for Advanced level. Animal behaviour is a subject which is increasingly studied at Sixth form level. It is one of the Joint Matriculation Board Advanced level Biology options, and is a special topic in Oxford Local Examinations Advanced level Zoology. This book should be useful to these candidates. It also covers a large section of the Associated Examining Board Advanced level Psychology syllabus.

One of the advantages of the study of animal behaviour at Sixth form level is that many practical exercises can be carried out without the need for expensive apparatus, and those in this book use only equipment which is usually available in schools. School laboratory experiments are almost impossible to accredit to any one originator. These experiments are not new or original, but have been found to give interesting and useful results in our biology courses over many years in this school. Invertebrates are easily obtainable for investigations, and domesticated and semi-domesticated animals can provide useful behaviour data. We all have constant social encounters with other people, which become even more interesting if seen from a behavioural standpoint.

A book such as this which includes a wide range of topics can consider some important aspects only briefly. We hope that by introducing such a wide range readers will be stimulated to follow up topics which interest them. At pre-university level some topics may particularly interest students aiming at medical courses; others may appeal to budding ethologists, physiologists or geneticists. Many articles about animal behaviour appear in journals such as the *New Scientist* and the *Scientific American* which will take the student further.

I should like to thank Dr. Geoffrey Parker of the University of Liverpool for reading various sections of the book in typescript. I have gratefully accepted his suggestions. Dr. Glenn Hayhurst, my colleague at Birkenhead High School, provided photographs, and also many enjoyable discussions over the years, and I thank him. Other photographs were very kindly supplied by B. Gadsby and P. Wallis of the Wildfowl Trust, Martin Mere, and by ESL. Bristol. My son, Mr John Brookfield, was also generous with his time in reading the typescript, and made useful and perceptive comments. The Editor of the series, Dr. M. B. V. Roberts has helped in many ways, and suggested many improvements to the manuscript which I have incorporated, and I am grateful to him. Any errors remaining are, of course, my responsibility. I would also like to thank my present and past Sixth form students; their interest in the subject has been most stimulating.

A. P. Brookfield

Contents

Acknowledgement is due to the following for permission to use copyright material as a basis for some of the illustrations in this book.

Cover photograph Aquila Photographs **page 9** *Principles of Animal Physiology*. 2nd edition. D. W. Wood (Edward Arnold.) **pages 11, 14** *Physiological Approach to Lower Animals*. 2nd edition. J. A. Ramsay 1972. (Cambridge University Press). **page 20, 21** Polarised – Light Navigation by Insects. R. Wehner. *Scientific American*. July 1976 **pages 24, 25** Based on Grenville: *Biology of the Individual*. 1971 Published by the Longman Group Limited. **page 28** The Zoological Society of London. **page 30** K. D. Roeder Scientific American April 1965 **page 38** How Animals Communicate. J. D. Carthy. *Discovery*. Oct 1964 **page 43** Biological Clocks. J. E. Harker. *Discovery*. April 1961 **pages 45, 47** Heidelberg Science Library. **page 59** From *Animal Behaviour* by R. A. Hinde. © 1970 Used with permission of McGraw-Hill Book Company. **pages 40, 63, 88** *The Life of Insects*. V. B. Wigglesworth. (Weidenfeld and Nicolson.) **pages 60, 62, 79** *The Study of Instinct*. N. Tinbergen. (Oxford University Press.) **page 70** Love in Infant Monkeys. H. F. Harlow. *Scientific American*. June 1959 **page 73** Imprinting in Animals. E. H. Hess. *Scientific American*. March 1958 **page 79** *Animal Behaviour* 8 Baillière Tindall. **page 91, 95** *Principles of Animal Psychology*. Maier and Schneirla. 1964 (Dover Publications Inc.) **pages 102, 103** © 1959 1971 American Psychological Association. Reprinted by permission. **page 105** *An introduction to the Study of Man*. J. Z. Young. (Oxford University Press). Hubel and Wiesel J. Physiol. 160 (1962) **page 119** *The Life of the Robin*. D. Lack, artist Robert Gillmor. (H. F. and G. Witherby Ltd.) **page 132** *The Insect Societies*. E. O. Wilson. 1971 (Harvard University Press.) Reprinted by permission **page 161** The Stellar-Orientation System of a Migratory Bird. S. T. Emlen. *Scientific American*. August 1975 **page 173** The Genetics of Behaviour in Brian M. Foss (ed): *New Horizons in Psychology 1*. Pelican Books, 1966) pp 193, 194. © Penguin Books, 1966. **page 173** *Introduction to Animal Behaviour* A. Manning (Edward Arnold) **page 177** *Genetics, Environment and Behaviour*. S. G. Vandenberg 1972 (Academic Press).

1 The techniques of study

Behaviour is the way in which an animal responds to its environment. Obviously such a definition covers an enormously wide field, and so the science of animal behaviour can be subdivided into various types of investigation.

Ethologists, for example, carry out zoologically orientated studies in which the investigator concentrates on the natural behaviour of the organism, and particularly its relationship with other members of the same species. Both neurophysiologists and psychologists study behaviour by means of laboratory experiments. Neurophysiologists have two basic approaches. In one, 'false' electrical impulses are fed into the nervous system by means of electrodes to see what type of behaviour can be elicited; in the other, various areas of the nervous system, particularly the brain of vertebrates, are electrically monitored while observable behaviour is taking place. Psychologists concentrate on problems of experience such as learning and conditioning, usually with domesticated species, in tests which can be carefully controlled.

Behaviour is also studied experimentally by endocrinologists. Just as neurophysiologists monitor the effect of changes in the nervous system, endocrinologists monitor behaviour changes produced by the endocrine system. Such behaviour changes may be produced naturally by seasonal variations in the size and the activity of endocrine organs such as the gonads, or may be experimentally produced by the removal, and subsequent replacement, of endocrine organs.

The genetic constitution of an organism is the basis for all its life processes and so one would expect there to be a genetic component to behavioural patterns. Such patterns are complex in vertebrates, and so much of the behavioural work of geneticists has been carried out in invertebrate species where more stereotyped and rigid behaviour occurs, and so variations from this rigid pattern are more clearly identified.

Many other disciplines are involved in present day behaviour studies. Ecologists try to understand the structure of populations and societies and their relationship with other populations in the community, and such ecological studies must include an understanding of population genetics and dynamics, and also animal behaviour. The latest aspect of animal behaviour studies is the formulation of the basic principles of socio-biology by Wilson. Socio-biology aims to amalgamate all aspects of social behaviour in human and non-human animals and to use such a synthesis to explain the underlying hereditary basis for social behaviour.

As we see, many different types of investigations, experiments and observations can be involved in present day animal behaviour studies. However in the past there have been problems in the interpretation of the experimental results or observations.

In 1894 Lloyd Morgan stated the principle which has since been named 'Morgan's Canon'. In this he says: 'In no case may we interpret an action as the outcome of a higher psychical faculty if it can be interpreted as the outcome of the exercise of one which stands lower in the psychological scale.' Such an axiom follows from that proposed by a fourteenth century Franciscan monk named William of Occam, which is now called Occam's razor. This states that, given the alternative between two hypotheses, the one accompanied by the fewer assumptions is to be preferred. By always working from the simplest possible interpretation of an action, it is easier to avoid the problems of anthropomorphism. Early investigators and observers of animal behaviour found it difficult to dissociate themselves from the activity they were watching and to interpret the behaviour pattern in other than human terms. Poorly observed phenomena such as the population cycles of small rodents entered the realms of folk-lore with tales of mass suicidal leaps of lemmings into the sea. Stories abounded of animals displaying almost all levels of human achievement from simple arithmetic to consciously thought out sacrificial mother love.

One of the classic cases of misinterpretation was that explaining the activities of 'Clever Hans', a horse belonging to Herr von Osten. German newspapers in 1904 reported that the horse could answer all manner of questions, either by moving its head for 'yes' or 'no', or by tapping its forefoot the correct number of times for numerical answers. Trickery and deliberate fraud were soon ruled out; Herr von Osten did not object to strangers putting questions to his horse, and it 'answered' just as well in his absence as in his presence. However if a question was asked by one person who then went away, and another person who had not heard the question counted up the number of foot taps made by the horse, it immediately became clear that the horse could not do arithmetic at all. It tapped its foot without stopping whilst constantly looking at the investigator. How 'Clever Hans' was clever was in responding to the infinitesimal movements made by the investigator when the correct number of foot taps had been reached. An amazing performance in perception, but not in arithmetic!

When the 'Clever Hans' episode had died away, the controversy about 'thinking animals' was reopened by the reputed arithmetical ability of what were called the 'Elberfeld horses'. This was a more complicated situation; three horses, Muhamed, Hanschen and Berto, were involved. However again it was found that the animals were responding to the almost imperceptible signals given by their keeper, Albert.

Investigators assumed that other organisms perceived their surroundings through sense organs which were fundamentally similar to those of man, both in structure and in the type of stimuli to which they responded. The reception and use of a form of energy for which man had no sense organs was regarded as almost miraculous.

Round about the beginning of this century some investigators were beginning to think that observation of animals in the field could only lead to unprovable suppositions about behaviour, and that a much more productive approach would be to place the animal in a contrived situation and then record the response made. Such experiments were used to very great effect by Pavlov in his work on the conditioned reflex. Other workers followed along this experimental line, and by the 1930s it was felt by many that the total behaviour shown by an animal could be interpreted as a linking together of small, fairly stereotyped responses to stimuli. Each small section could be analysed and explained in terms of the working of the nervous system, and the whole is nothing more than the sum of reflexes and other automatic responses. Such was the original position of the Behaviourist school, an important investigator being B. F. Skinner. We shall return to consider both Pavlov and Skinner in Chapter 10.

However other investigators turned away from such contrived, and necessarily simplistic, situations and began to study how animals behaved in natural situations. Pioneer ethologists like Lorenz, Tinbergen and von Frisch moved along the pathways of patient observation laid down by Fabre in the nineteenth century. Fabre studied the life history, habits and instincts of insects by extremely careful observation, and although his interpretation of their behaviour is not what would be made nowadays, he amassed a large amount of factual data by a lifetime of patient study.

Modern ethologists are constantly aware of the problems involved in recording aspects of an observed behaviour pattern. Word descriptions can be ambiguous and subconsciously biassed. Sometimes the observed behaviour can be dealt with numerically such as the frequency of occurrence, or its intensity on an arbitrary scale, or its duration, and then the data amassed can be subjected to statistical analysis. Nowadays it is possible to record a behaviour pattern by many types of mechanical aid. Cinematography enables a sequence to be watched repeatedly, at various frame speeds, and analysed into specific limited movements.

Infra-red cameras may be used to film animals which are nocturnal and which do not react to the infra-red transmission. Very fast movements may be apparently slowed down by the use of multiple flash photography.

There are also mechanical aids which will monitor movement without the investigator needing to be present. These include photo-electric cells placed near nests or breeding sites, and various kinds of activity recorders or actographs. (Figure 1)

FIGURE 1

A   Wheel counter.
A projection from a treadmill type running wheel makes contact at every revolution with a switch in a circuit which activates a counter.
B   Point Actograph.
The drum is balanced on a central point. As the animal moves around different switches are activated and a record is made. In this case the animal moved from sections 1 to 5.
C   Knife edge actograph.
Any movement from one end of the container to the other is recorded on the moving drum.

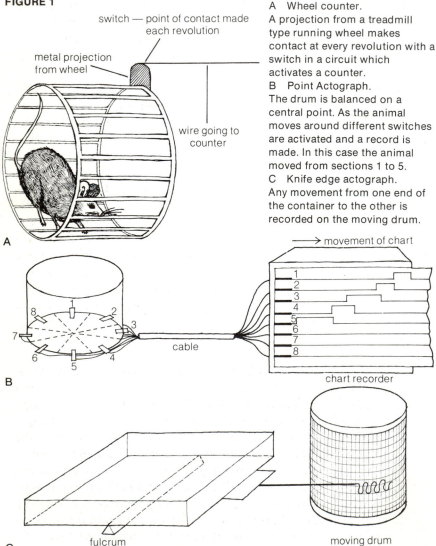

However these mechanical aids, although very useful, are still limited. There may well be alterations in the environment to which other organisms respond which we cannot perceive, and therefore do not look for. In scientific experiments the investigator would normally manipulate one factor, the independent variable, and see what happens to another, the dependent variable. Such an experimental situation is relatively easy to arrange in the physical sciences, but it is quite a different matter with living organisms. There may be numerous small differences both within the conditions surrounding experimental organisms and within the organisms themselves. If, for instance, we wish to find the effect of changing the wavelength of incident light on the behaviour of earthworms, we must not overlook the possibility that we are also changing the environmental temperature. Similarly one must accept that genetic variability between organisms in the population studied could have effects on their behaviour patterns. A very careful approach to experimental design helps to eliminate problems of the first type, with a control set up along with the experimental situation. Ideally if we know that there are N factors operating, then the control would contain all N factors, and the experimental situation would keep $N-1$ factors constant, and vary the remaining one.

The second problem could be overcome by using clones of organisms. In some animals asexual reproduction and so the production of offspring with identical genotypes is part of their normal life cycle, and so these organisms make useful experimental subjects. However the study of animal behaviour is to find out how all animals behave, not just those which happen to fit conveniently into some experimental situation. We must find other ways to eliminate the effects of genetic variance. We can try to do this by random sampling and there are various techniques which can be used to ensure that one does obtain a truly random sample of organisms. The sample chosen must be of a suitable size before one can make general deductions from it. No investigator would reach conclusions about the normal behaviour of students in general by carefully watching and recording every movement made by one particular person throughout the course of a day; a very much larger sample would be needed. Even if a sample is large enough to reveal distinctive behaviour patterns, one must not extrapolate from these results to cover the population in general, or even the non-student population of the same age as the sample. All of this seems obvious, but it illustrates the difficulty of drawing conclusions about behavioural patterns from too small an observed sample of organisms.

No matter which behaviour pattern is being investigated however, we must try to understand the basic physiology of the animal concerned. The capacity to react to environmental change requires sensitivity of a particular part of the animal, and a response in what may well be a different part. The sensitive region, or receptor, must be connected in some way with the responding region, or effector. In the simplest organisms, the protists, transmission takes place within the single cell, but in higher organisms a nervous system, made of cells specialised for this transmission, is present. The pattern of neural organisation depends on the type of symmetry found in the organism, and this we shall consider in the next chapter.

2 Neural organisation in invertebrates

The two basic patterns of symmetry, radial and bilateral symmetry, can be clearly seen in invertebrates.

RADIAL SYMMETRY

Radially symmetrical animals have a circular organisation with a central mouth. This means that they can be cut vertically into two identical pieces; they cannot, however, be cut horizontally into two similar sections as one only of these sections will encompass the mouth. Radial symmetry has evolved in two main phyla – the coelenterates and the echinoderms. Such a circular pattern means that any part of the circumference of the animal can lead in progressive movement, and so one would expect that any sense organs would be arranged equidistantly around the edge of the organism. This is, in fact, what is found.

Coelenterates are diploblastic animals which can exist either as sedentary polyps or as free swimming medusae.(Figure 2)

It is thought that the most primitive form was a type of medusa, and that the polyp originally was a transitory stage in the primitive life cycle. Some coelenterates pass through both medusa and polyp stages during their life cycle, but others live permanently either as polyps or as medusae.

Such variation in mobility between the free swimming medusae and the slower moving or stationary polyps is correlated with differences in their neural organisation.

In coelenterates most of the nervous system consists of a nerve net made up of multipolar neurones which can transmit impulses in all

FIGURE 2

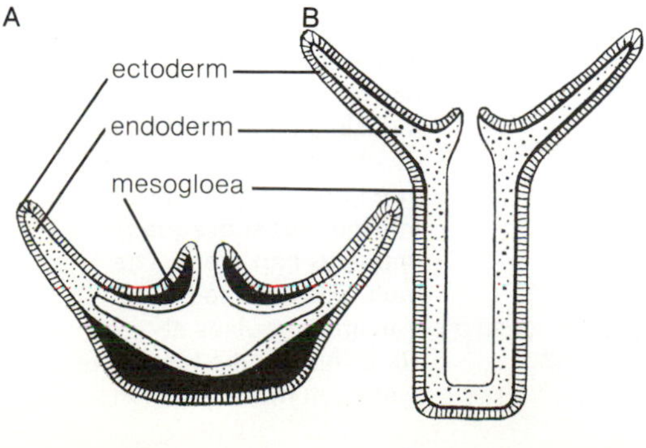

A

B

ectoderm

endoderm

mesogloea

Medusa and polyp forms of coelenterates – vertical sections.
A   medusa.
B   polyp.
The basic body plan is similar although the dimensions of the tissue layers vary.

directions. In the larger coelenterates such as sea anemones and jelly-fish there are regions where the nerve net is concentrated into definite tracts where the neurones are bipolar. Conduction within these neurones is much faster; speeds of $2\,\mathrm{m\,s^{-1}}$ may be reached compared with $10\,\mathrm{cm\,s^{-1}}$ in the general nerve net. Fast through conduction systems are found wherever fast co-ordinated movement is needed, such as round the oral disc for feeding, or in the column of anemones for defensive reflexes, or in the umbrella of medusae to produce swimming movements. (Figure 3)

FIGURE 3

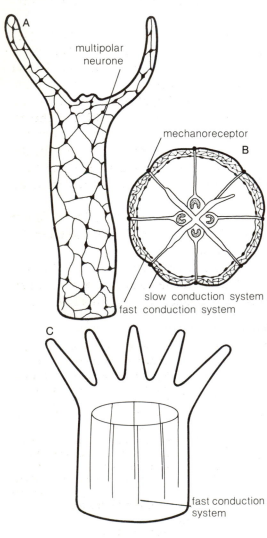

Coelenterate nervous systems.
A   The nerve net of *Hydra*, made up of multipolar neurones.
An impulse, generated in one neurone, fails to cross the synapse to adjacent neurones but has a facilitating effect so that a second impulse can get across the synaptic gap. By this interneural facilitation excitation spreads throughout the nerve net.
B   Nervous system of *Aurelia*, the common jelly fish.
Here there are two nerve nets, one made from multipolar neurones and giving the same type of slow response that is seen in *Hydra*, and one consisting of bipolar neurones with much faster transmission.
C   Nervous system of sea-anemone.
The tentacles have a nerve net made from multipolar neurones. There is also a fast conduction system of bipolar neurones which lie in the vertical mesenteric muscle sheets. Facilitation occurs in this system between the neurones and the muscle cells, the first impulse to reach the neuromuscular junction failing to pass into the muscle, but subsequent impulses can cross. The multi-polar nerve net can transmit impulses at 10–$20\,\mathrm{cm\,s^{-1}}$; the fast nerve system at more than $1\,\mathrm{m\,s^{-1}}$.

Labels in figure: multipolar neurone; mechanoreceptor; B; slow conduction system; fast conduction system; C; fast conduction system

A sea anemone does not normally respond if the base of the column is subjected to a single electric shock. However if a second shock is given within 0.2 to 2.5 seconds of the first then the column contracts. If a series of shocks is given within this time range, contraction is greater still. It is thought that the first impulse can travel through the bipolar neurones, which make up the fast conduction system, as far as the nerve-muscle junction but no further. However even though the impulse cannot pass, it has altered the chemistry of the neurone ending in such a way that a second impulse can get across the nerve-muscle junction as long as it occurs within a particular time span. Such a process is called facilitation; in this case it is neuro-muscular facilitation. (Figure 4)

If the tentacle of a sea anemone is touched once, it will withdraw. If it is then repeatedly touched the other tentacles will gradually respond until eventually all the tentacles are withdrawn. In this case facilitation between the multipolar neurones is involved. The single impulse reaches only to the first synapse; the second impulse can pass across the now facilitated synapse to the neurones in contact; the third reaches to the next neurones and so eventually impulses pass throughout the whole nerve net. Such a gradual spreading out of a response from the point of stimulation is known as decremental conduction. At any time the strength of the response is inversely related to its distance from the stimulated area.

These two types of response – one strong and rapid, the other gradually developing throughout the whole animal – depend upon the characteristics of the neurones involved.

Echinoderms are relatively advanced invertebrates, most of which can move around, if somewhat slowly. The nervous system of a starfish consists of an oral nerve ring surrounding the central mouth from

FIGURE 4

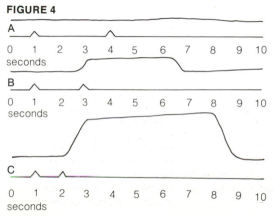

Facilitation in the sea anemone. Contractions of the column in response to electric shocks were recorded on a moving drum.

A   Two shocks were given three seconds apart. The column did not contract.

B   Contraction occurs to the second of two shocks given two seconds apart.

C   Contraction is greater if the second shock is given only one second after the first.

Based on Wood.

which a radial nerve tract runs down each arm. These nerve tracts link up with the peripheral nerve net lying just under the ectoderm. The oral ring seems to control the direction of movement – without it each arm moves independently. If the oral ring is cut into two parts, then the corresponding halves of the starfish move away from each other. If all the radial nerves are cut the starfish shows poor co-ordination. However even in this state it is still able to turn itself over if reversed, and this suggests that the peripheral nerve net takes over.

BILATERAL SYMMETRY

Bilateral symmetry is the general type found both in invertebrates and in vertebrates. The development of an anterior end means that it samples the environment into which the animal is moving and many sense organs have evolved there. This is correlated with an increased complexity of the nervous system in the head to deal with the increased input of information from these sense organs. Such a development is called cephalisation, and it usually involves the concentration of nerve cells to make ganglia or a primitive brain. From these anterior ganglia, nerve cords pass along the length of the body.

Platyhelminthes are flatworms which may be free living or parasitic. The nervous system of *Planaria*, a typical free living platyhelminth, consists essentially of a nerve net as in *Hydra*, but with the important development of paired cerebral ganglia and two distinct longitudinal nerve cords. From experimental removal of the cerebral ganglia we can conclude that the nerve net is responsible for muscle movement, the cerebral ganglia acting as a relay system which passes impulses from the sense organs to the nerve net. Such an arrangement allows more complex behaviour than is possible with the diffuse nerve net of *Hydra*. Parasitic platyhelminthes tend to have less well developed nervous systems than do free living flatworms, and usually lack special sense organs.

Platyhelminthes are simple acoelomate, nonsegmented animals. The true segmented worms, the annelids, show many evolutionary advances over the platyhelminthes. They are coelomate animals with well developed alimentary canals which have a mouth and an anus. The nervous system shows a greater tendency to cephalisation and centralisation than in platyhelminthes. The paired cerebral ganglia now lie above the pharynx, and so are named the supra-pharyngeal ganglia, and they connect with a sub-pharyngeal ganglion by circum-pharyngeal nerve cords. From the sub-pharyngeal ganglion a ventral nerve cord, apparently made by the fusion of two longitudinal nerve cords, runs along the length of the body, beneath the gut. This ventral nerve cord contains a series of segmentally arranged reflex arcs. In the muscle wall there are stretch receptors, the axons from which pass to the ventral nerve cord. Here the axons make synaptic connections with motor neurones which innervate the muscles of the same segment, but also with internuncial neurones which can pass the impulses to motor neurones in adjacent segments. (Figure 5)

Such an arrangement can explain the passage of the peristaltic waves of contraction which bring about forward movement in the earthworm. Contraction of the longitudinal muscles in one segment will stimulate the stretch receptors in the next segment. By a reflex action the muscles in this segment will now contract, thereby stimulating the stretch receptors in the next segment, and so on. This requires only the presence of intra-segmental reflex arcs, and this accounts for the experimental evidence that if a worm is completely cut in half, and is then stitched together again, peristaltic movement will continue normally. However in a further experiment a worm was severed apart from the nerve cord, and the segments each side of the cut were pinned down so securely that they could not act as mechanical stimuli for each other. Peristaltic waves of contraction still passed over the cut and so in this case another explanation is needed. Here the alternative pathway using the internuncial neurones is used to produce inter-segmental reflexes. Stimulation of the stretch receptor in one segment will start a chain reaction in which the impulse will pass to the motor neurone of the next segment. There a motor response will stimulate the receptor of that segment, and so the reaction will pass down the body. However the number of segments knocked out of action by being pinned down is

FIGURE 5

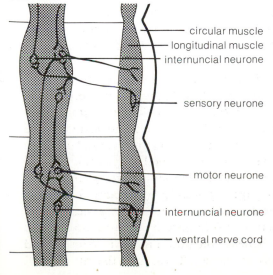

circular muscle
longitudinal muscle
internuncial neurone

sensory neurone

motor neurone

internuncial neurone

ventral nerve cord

Some neurone relationships in the earthworm.
The sensory neurones are stretch receptors, and the impulses which leave them travel both to the motor neurones of the same segment, and to internuncial neurones connecting with adjacent segments.

critical. If more than three segments are involved, the peristaltic wave stops, and so it appears that constant reinforcement from the stretch receptors is necessary.

Reflex actions brought about by such means are adequate to produce the slow peristaltic movement shown by earthworms. However earthworms are capable of making very fast escape movements, withdrawing into their soil burrows too quickly for either hungry birds or ardent naturalists to catch them. So a third type of neural organisation must be available to the worm, which does not depend on very thin short nerve fibres and the consequent synaptic delays. Such a system is found in the three giant fibres which lie on the dorsal surface of the nerve cord. The median fibre is 160 micrometres in diameter and can transmit impulses at up to 45 m s^{-1}. The two lateral fibres are 60 micrometres in diameter and can transmit at 10 m s^{-1}. Each giant fibre is made up by the fusion of the axons of many nerve cells. Although there are giant synapses along the length of the giant fibres, these do not delay the passage of the nerve impulse. The two lateral fibres are connected to each other by pathways of low resistance in certain segments, and an

FIGURE 6

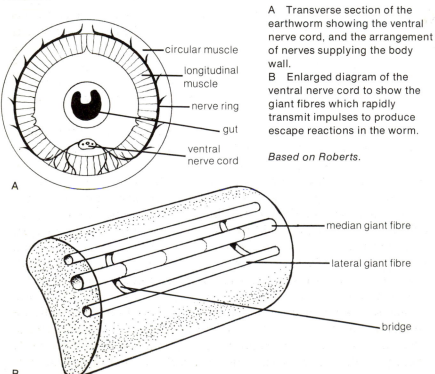

circular muscle

longitudinal muscle

nerve ring

gut

ventral nerve cord

A   Transverse section of the earthworm showing the ventral nerve cord, and the arrangement of nerves supplying the body wall.
B   Enlarged diagram of the ventral nerve cord to show the giant fibres which rapidly transmit impulses to produce escape reactions in the worm.

Based on Roberts.

A

median giant fibre

lateral giant fibre

bridge

B

impulse in one spreads rapidly to the other. The median fibre is structurally and physiologically isolated from these two lateral fibres. Nerve fibres run out from the giant fibres to the longitudinal muscles in each segment. The median fibre is activated by sense organs within the first forty anterior segments and directs all chaetae forwards, thus driving the worm backwards. The lateral fibres connected with sense organs in the posterior section of the worm, direct the chaetae backwards and so drive the worm forwards. So the worm can escape from impending attack at either end. (Figure 6)

Earthworms are slow moving, burrowing animals and their mode of life is very different from that of their close relatives, the polychaetes. Many polychaetes are free swimming animals, and in these cephalisation has proceeded further; mobility is correlated with highly developed anterior sense organs, and there is a corresponding increase in complexity of the supra-pharyngeal ganglion.

This annelid pattern of neural organisation is found, but with important advances, in the arthropods. The supra-pharyngeal ganglion or brain shows more differentiation, with large nerves connecting it with the eyes and antennae. The ventral nerve cord consists of segmental ganglia joined by double longitudinal connectives, the thoracic ganglia being larger than the abdominal. A sympathetic system supplying the muscles of the gut and the spiracles is present. The brain acts partly as a sensory relay station passing impulses from the sense organs to the relevant effector organs. A grasshopper without a brain shows incessant activity of its mouthparts and legs, and will jump or fly at the slightest stimulation. Although the brain does not directly co-ordinate muscle activity – as we see, a decerebrate insect can still walk, jump or fly – it has an inhibitory control.

Annelids and arthropods are segmented animals and this segmentation is obvious in their neural organisation. Molluscs however are non-segmented and so the nervous system has altered in form. In cephalopods like the squid and the octopus the nervous system shows its highest development in invertebrates. The large brain above the oesophagus may contain many millions of nerve cells, and so internal differentiation is possible. The octopus brain and its sub-oesophageal section can be subdivided into about thirty anatomically distinct lobes, and their contribution to the behaviour of the animal have been investigated both by electrical stimulation of the particular area, and by the effect of removing or lesioning the part. Giant fibres, which as we have already seen are important as a fast relay system in the annelids, are present in a more complicated system in cephalopods. Three series of fibres are involved in the sudden, violent contraction of the muscle making up the mantle wall which helps the animal to escape from danger. Normally water is drawn into the mantle cavity, circulated over the gills and then gently expelled. However in the escape response the water is expelled with such force that the animal is moved in the opposite direction. (Figure 7)

The first pair of giant fibres lies within the brain; second order fibres run from the brain to the stellate ganglia on each side of the mantle; from here the third order fibres run to the muscles. There is a graded difference in the diameter of these third order fibres; those which have the furthest distance to go are thicker, and therefore transmit their impulses faster than the short fibres. This gives simultaneous contraction of all the muscle blocks, and a more powerful thrust. This jet propulsion system can produce very powerful movement. The flying squid, *Onchoteuthis banksii*, can leave the water fast enough to remain airborne for several seconds, during which time it may have glided for fifty yards.

This necessarily condensed outline of neural organisation in invertebrates can show only selected organisms and phyla, but a general evolutionary trend towards specialisation, and, in the bilaterally symmetrical organisms towards cephalisation becomes clear. As we have said, cephalisation is usually correlated with the concentration of sense organs at the leading end of the organism, and it is to sense organs that we now turn.

FIGURE 7

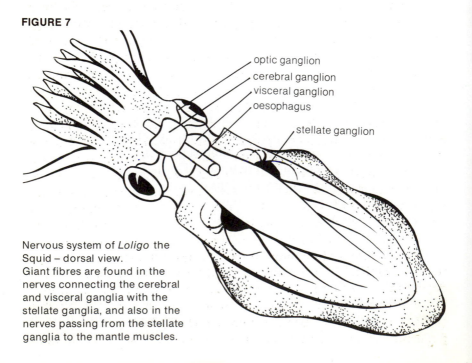

optic ganglion
cerebral ganglion
visceral ganglion
oesophagus
stellate ganglion

Nervous system of *Loligo* the Squid – dorsal view.
Giant fibres are found in the nerves connecting the cerebral and visceral ganglia with the stellate ganglia, and also in the nerves passing from the stellate ganglia to the mantle muscles.

3 Sense organs

Each particular species lives in a 'world' of its own for an animal can only perceive the environment through what its senses can tell it. This idea was summarised in 1909 by Jacob von Uekhull in the word *umwelt* or outer world. Even protists, the simplest of animals, show clear irritability. Unicells will respond to such stimuli as an alteration in the light intensity or the pH of the surrounding medium. *Euglena*, for example, will move towards a higher light intensity, and *Paramecium* towards regions of higher acidity. Even with such small organisms there may be all the components present of a reflex action; a receptor, some form of transmission and an effector. In *Euglena* there is a light sensitive eyespot and some method of contracting present within the single cell.

In more advanced organisms the sensitive regions may be found within sensory cells scattered over the surface, or they may be gathered together to form special sense organs. Each sense organ is a biological transducer in that it converts the energy of the stimulus into a standard nerve impulse. Light, for example, is detected as photons by a photochemical pigment which is specialised to respond to the energy levels of specific wavelengths; heat is detected by the absorption of quanta of a different energy level; electricity by the energy of electrons; tastes and smells by chemical energy; sound by molecular movement.

No matter which type of sensory cell is involved in the initiation of the nerve impulse, there are certain characteristics which they all have in common. On stimulation there is a change in the ionic relationships of the cell membrane and this produces a local electric charge called the generator potential. If this generator potential builds up to a certain value, the threshold value, then an impulse will pass along the nerve fibre. A second impulse will then follow if the stimulation of the sensory cell continues, followed by a third, and so on. Weak stimulation will result in few impulses passing, strong stimulation in a much greater frequency of impulse initiation. However if stimulation continues there may be a falling off in impulse frequency, until the sensory cell stops firing altogether. This is adaptation and the time taken for it to occur depends upon the type of sensory cell and the task it has to perform.

Receptors which provide information about the very variable external environment (exteroceptors) are usually highly sensitive, and frequently adapt quickly to cut down information about continuous processes. Tactile receptors within the human skin adapt extremely quickly; one rapidly loses the sensation of pressure from one's clothing after dressing in the morning. Conditions within the body are relatively stable, and the internal receptors (enteroceptors) are less sensitive. Enteroceptors may need to go on sending information over a long period; posture is maintained by impulses from muscle spindles and so it is important that these receptors should not adapt.

It is thought that sensory adaptation results from a gradual change in the cell membrane which prevents the ionic exchanges necessary for the generator potential to build up to the threshold value. As sensory adaptation results in the loss of the power to initiate impulses because of continual stimulation, one would expect a similar situation to arise in a post-synaptic nerve cell. A high frequency series of impulses arriving at a synapse over a long period is eventually blocked there; the post-synaptic cell has accommodated, and needs time to recover before it can again transmit.

In some receptors, adaptation is seen to be related to their morphology. Pacinian corpuscles (a figure appears later) respond to pressure, and adapt very quickly. The nerve ending within is surrounded by concentric layers of cells which are deformed by pressure; the layers of cells however rapidly return to their original shape and no longer affect the nerve ending.

LIGHT RECEPTORS

Visible light, to man, is that part of the electromagnetic spectrum lying between 380 and 760 nm wavelength. Other organisms, such as the honey bee, have eyes which can receive much shorter wavelengths in the ultra-violet region. As the colours which we see when looking at a coloured flower depend on which wavelengths are reflected and which absorbed by the pigments in the petals, it is not surprising that, in flowers which depend for pollination on bees, there are also ultra-violet 'pigments' present. Various species of *Potentilla*, for example, exhibit patterns when photographed under ultra-violet radiation of 370 nm which are not seen using visible light of higher wavelength. So we must not assume that what is seen by man is also what is seen by other organisms.

Light receptors are widespread in animals. The simplest form of receptor is a light sensitive region within a cell. In *Euglena* the light sensitive region is at the base of the flagellum. Such a sensitive region is made more valuable to the organism by the presence, in the cytoplasm nearby, of a pigment spot containing carotenoids. It is advantageous to *Euglena* to move towards regions of high light intensity as it is a photosynthetic organism. In unilateral light, the sensitive eye-spot is

FIGURE 8

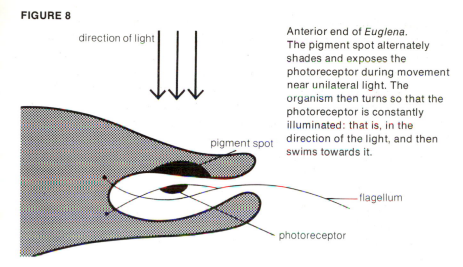

direction of light

pigment spot

flagellum

photoreceptor

Anterior end of *Euglena*. The pigment spot alternately shades and exposes the photoreceptor during movement near unilateral light. The organism then turns so that the photoreceptor is constantly illuminated: that is, in the direction of the light, and then swims towards it.

alternately shaded and exposed to light as the organism spirals forward. When this happens the anterior region bends towards the light source and the organism can then swim towards it. (Figure 8)

The light receptors of earthworms are of the diffuse kind with single light sensitive cells, the light cells of Hess, scattered within the skin, particularly on the dorsal surfaces of the anterior and posterior segments. Such an arrangement is sufficient for a burrowing animal but surface living animals need to appreciate the direction of light as well as its intensity. This is achieved by a concentration of sensitive cells in certain regions of the organism and the presence of pigment cells which screen the sensitive cells from incident light in other than one direction. Such specialised regions can be called eyes, and an evolutionary trend of increasing complexity can be seen in invertebrates, from coelenterates up to the extremely well organised eyes of cephalopod molluscs. (Figure 9 see next page)

A cephalopod eye is similar in many superficial ways to a vertebrate eye, but there are important differences which arise during the embryological development of the two types. In the cephalopod the eye originates as an ectodermal pit, the lining forming the retina and the contents forming the vitreous humour. Nerve fibres leave the retina on its convex surface. The vertebrate retina is formed from an outgrowth from the brain which becomes cup-shaped, and nerve fibres run along the concave surface of this cup until they pass through it to form the optic nerve. In the vertebrate eye, the lens is formed in one movement by the thickening and intucking of the ectoderm over the developing

FIGURE 9

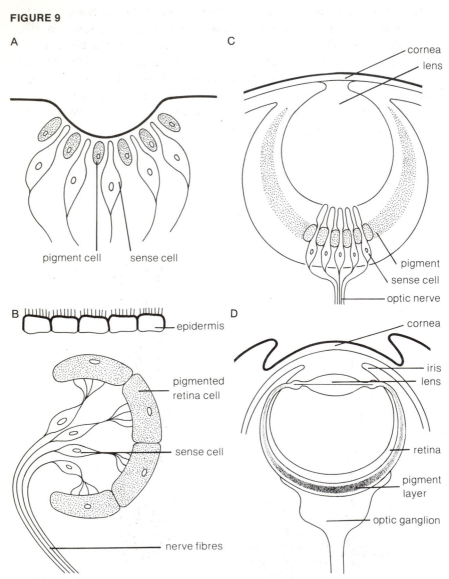

A   Coelenterate eye – in the medusa of *Lizzia koellikeri*.
There are eight eyes, each of which is a patch of ectoderm in which some cells have developed pigment, and others have elongated to make rods.
B   Platyhelminth eye – *Planaria*.
The epidermis over the eyes is non-pigmented and so allows light to pass through. There are varying numbers of sense cells, the fibrillae from which touch the pigmented retina cells. *Planaria lugubris* has two sense cells, *Planaria lactea* has thirty.
C   Annelid eye – the polychaete *Nereis*. The eye has become very cup-shaped, and seems to be like a pin-hole camera although it is not known if image formation is possible. The sense cells are rod-like and there is a pigment layer.
D   Mollusc eye – the cephalopod *Sepia*. – for description see text.

retinal cup, whereas it is clearly in two halves in the cephalopod. The inner section is formed from the eyeball and the outer section is formed from the body epithelium, at the time of the growth of the circular iris and cornea. The mechanism of accommodation is also different; the cephalopod moves the lens backwards and forwards as in a camera, whereas the higher vertebrates alter the curvature and therefore the strength of the lens. Nevertheless the two types of eyes show striking evolutionary convergence. (Figure 10)

FIGURE 10

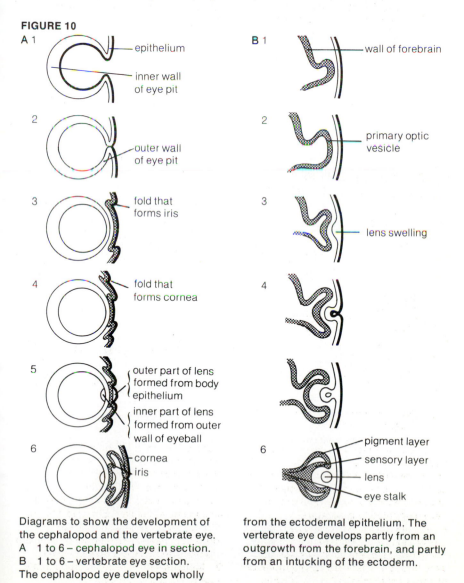

Diagrams to show the development of the cephalopod and the vertebrate eye.
A   1 to 6 – cephalopod eye in section.
B   1 to 6 – vertebrate eye section.
The cephalopod eye develops wholly from the ectodermal epithelium. The vertebrate eye develops partly from an outgrowth from the forebrain, and partly from an intucking of the ectoderm.

The compound eyes of arthropods do not fit into the evolutionary trend shown by other invertebrates, and work on an entirely different principle. Instead of a cup shaped retina with a lens, the eye is made up of a collection of elements named ommatidia, each consisting of a small number of sensitive cells grouped together with a double lens system at their outer end. The sensitive cells are separated from those in neighbouring ommatidia by pigment cells. (Figure 11)

Recent investigations in bees and ants have shown that there are nine visual cells in each ommatidium. Of these nine cells, eight are very long and make up most of the visual unit, and the ninth is very short and is at the inner end. Each visual cell has rows of microvilli on its inner surface, and these microvilli collectively make up the light sensitive region called the rhabdome. Rhodopsin molecules are arranged parallel to the long axes of the microvilli, unlike their random orientation within the membrane system of the retinal rod cells of vertebrates. (Figure 12)

Physiological and anatomical studies have shown that three of the nine visual cells in each ommatidium are ultra-violet receptors: the short cell and two of the long ones. The two long cells are opposite to each other in the ommatidium, and their microvilli, and so their rhodopsin molecules, are aligned in a straight line. One of the long cells becomes much thinner at the inner end of the ommatidium, and its

FIGURE 11

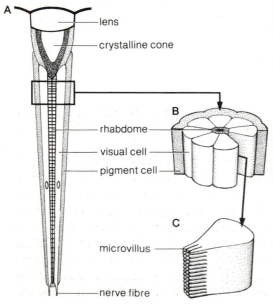

A lens
crystalline cone

B
rhabdome
visual cell
pigment cell

C
microvillus

nerve fibre

A   Longitudinal section of an ommatidium.
Each ommatidium has an outer layer of pigment cells surrounding a cylinder made of visual cells. The visual cells have microvilli on their inner edges, which together make up the light-sensitive region, the rhabdome. Within the microvilli the rhodopsin molecules are arranged parallel to the long axes, and this aids the absorption of polarised light.
B   Section of one optical unit. The pigment cells have been omitted on one side to show the arrangement of the visual cells.
C   Section of one visual cell showing the microvilli.

FIGURE 12

A

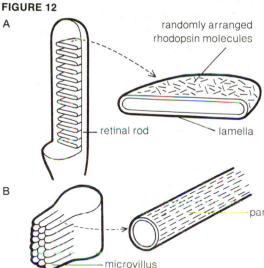

randomly arranged rhodopsin molecules

retinal rod

lamella

B

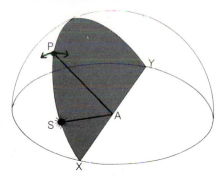

microvillus

parallel rhodopsin molecules

Visual cells of vertebrates and insects.
A Retinal rod cell of vertebrate eye.
B Part of visual cell from insect ommatidium.
In the retinal rod the rhodopsin molecules are randomly arranged. In the ommatidial cell they are parallel to the long axes of the microvilli.

Based on Wehner

FIGURE 13

The celestial hemisphere showing the direction of polarisation.
A plane of a great circle passes through the three points A, P and S, where A is the observing animal, P is the point observed and S is the position of the sun. X and Y are horizon points.

place is taken by the short cell. Such an alignment of molecules could provide a mechanism for the reception of polarised light, that is light vibrating in a particular direction.

When light passes through a gas the incident unpolarised wave, vibrating in all directions at right angles to its direction of movement, may become polarised (Figure 13). So unpolarised light leaving the sun becomes polarised as a result of scattering by molecules in the earth's atmosphere. At any point in the sky the light waves vibrate in a specific direction. The vibration direction is always at right angles to the plane of a triangle formed by the sun, S, the observer, A, and the point observed, P. This means that if the observing animal can detect the direction of polarisation in an area of clear sky, then it can also find the position of the sun, even if this is obscured.

When polarised light falls on the visual cells, it is maximally absorbed by those molecules of rhodopsin which are parallel to the polarisation direction. Surprisingly it was found that the cells which make up the visual unit of the ommatidium follow a twisted pattern, the cylinder made of the eight long cells doing a complete 180° turn from its end nearer the lens to its other end. This means that the rhodopsin molecules face all ways during the turn and so sensitivity to polarised light is lost. The short ninth cell however, being short, is twisted much less and so retains its polarisation receptivity. Some ommatidia show clockwise twists; others are twisted in an anticlockwise direction. Two adjacent ommatidia of opposite twist can therefore make up a working polarisation detector. In one the short cell deals with light polarised over a particular direction; the other covers a different range. One ultra-violet receptor which has lost its polarisation sensitivity gives a base line signal with which the other signals are compared.

By painting over different sections of the eyes of desert ants, it has been found there is a small region near the upper edge of each compound eye which is responsible for detecting polarised light. In one series of experiments, the lower part of the ant's visual field was blacked out by a screen held by the investigator, and the ant's behaviour was not affected until the blackout reached the lower edge of the polarised light receptor region. When the screen was lifted higher, the ant compensated by lifting its head up. As the screen was moved even higher, the tilt of the head became greater, until eventually the ant did a complete backwards somersault.

THERMORECEPTORS

Thermoreceptors are important in animals such as mammals as part of their homeostatic control of body temperature. Nerve endings near the skin surface respond to temperature changes, and inform the hypothalamus of conditions at skin level. Appropriate reflex action can then be taken: constriction of skin blood vessels and increased muscular movement in shivering maintains the normal body temperature in cold conditions, and dilation of skin blood vessels and increased sweating have the effect of cooling the body in hot conditions.

In some animals, however, thermoreceptors have become organs of special sense. The American rattle snake has a pit on each side of its head between the nostril and the eye, which contains cells which are extremely sensitive to infra-red radiation. A prey animal in the vicinity of the rattle snake may be sensed by the heat it produces. Some parasitic insects find their hosts in a similar way. The bed-bug, *Cimex*, and the large South American blood sucking bug *Rhodnius* have very sensitive thermoreceptors in their antennae and can find the way to their victims by means of the heat the victims produce. If a hungry *Rhodnius* is kept in a glass vessel it approaches those parts of the glass which have been warmed by the investigator's hands, but loses this behaviour if the antennae are amputated.

Such heat sensitive mechanisms have been copied by the designers of anti-aircraft missiles which 'home' onto their target aircraft by means of the heat produced by the aircraft engines.

ELECTRICITY RECEPTORS

Organs producing large electric pulses are found in certain fishes, such as the electric ray, *Torpedo*, and the South American electric eel, *Electrophorus*, which is not a true eel. Such organs are derived from muscle tissue modified to form sheet like plates, which act like a number of batteries in series. The pulses they produce may be of over 500 volts. These lethal discharges are of obvious value to the fish. There are, however, other fish which constantly emit electrical discharges which are too weak to use on prey. One particular order of fresh water fish from Africa, the *Mormyriformes*, all possess weak electric organs. *Gymnarchus*, for example, emits electrical discharges at 300 per second from an electric organ on its finless tail. During each discharge the head becomes oppositely charged to the tail and so a dipole field is set up around the fish. The skin of *Gymnarchus* is thick and nonconducting but there are many electroreceptors on and near the head. Each consists of a pore leading into a jelly-filled tube which extends into a capsule with sensory epithelium at its base. *Gymnarchus* is extremely sensitive to anything which disturbs its electric field. When kept in a laboratory tank it will react to a small magnet or even to the amount of static electricity on a comb held outside the tank.

CHEMORECEPTORS

Reaction to chemicals in the environment is found throughout the animal kingdm. At the unicell level chemicals are attractive or aversive to the organism, although the type of response also depends on the chemical concentration. *Paramecium* will avoid strong acids which could be harmful, but moves towards regions of slight acidity. This is valuable behaviour as the bacteria on which *Paramecium* feeds produce carbon dioxide which slightly acidifies the water.

Specialised chemoreceptors are of two basic forms, although it is somewhat difficult to differentiate between them. We use the term olfaction for the reception of minute concentrations of chemicals carried over large distances usually through gases, and gustation for the reception of chemicals through a liquid medium, that is, for smell and taste respectively. Such a distinction holds true for terrestrial animals such as man, but even here reception of the two types of stimuli, can be difficult to separate, as you will realise when you try to enjoy food while you have a bad cold in the nose. In aquatic animals such as fish there is a greater difficulty as all the stimulating particles are dissolved, or suspended in water. Olfaction occurs in organs innervated by the olfactory nerves, and gustation in the taste buds which are innervated by different nerves.

An olfactory sense which works over a distance is useful to an animal looking for food, but it is clear that many aspects of an organism's life depend on an efficient chemoreceptor system. Chemical communication by means of pheromones is common throughout the animal kingdom, and some animals such as insects depend upon the production and reception of chemicals which may act as sex attractants or may control social organisation. The sense organs involved are usually on the antennae, which may be highly branched. Taste receptors may be found on insect mouthparts, but are also on the feet of many insects. (Figure 14)

One of the problems of categorising chemical stimuli is that they cannot be quantified. There have been many attempts by sensory physiologists to compile a 'smell spectrum', but the variations of chemical structure found in volatile molecules makes such a task extremely difficult.

FIGURE 14

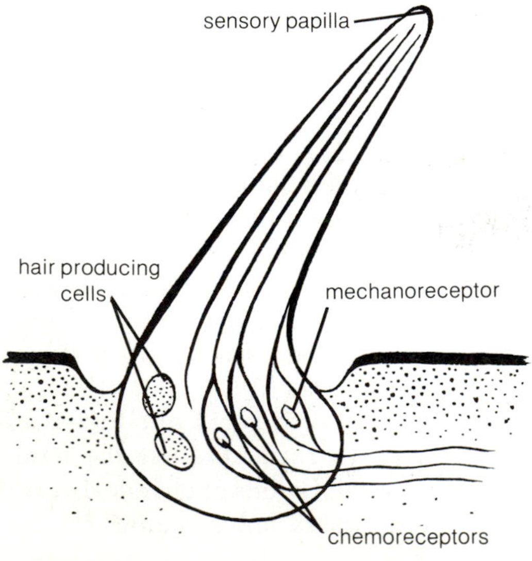

sensory papilla

hair producing cells

mechanoreceptor

chemoreceptors

An insect 'taste hair', – from the tarsus of *Phormia*, a blowfly. The 'taste hair' is a double organ, reacting to mechanical displacement and to chemical contact.
A small group of sense cells is found at the base of the hair. Nerve fibres pass from at least two cells to the sensory papilla at the tip of the hair – these are chemoreceptors. One further cell makes contact with the base of the hair and so acts as a typical mechanoreceptor.

MECHANORECEPTORS

A mechanoreceptor is a sense organ which is specialised to r̶
mechanical stimulation such as pressure or deformation. It usuaily
consists of one or more sensitive cells, each of which has a fine
projection which is stimulated in some mechanical way. Simple
mechanoreceptors, consisting of single sense cells, are found in insects,
and here there must be provision for their stimulation through
specialised thin sections of the rigid cuticle. There are many types, but
we shall consider two. (Figure 15)

Trichoid sensilla, being attached to bristles, can give the insect
information about displacement of the bristle, and campaniform sensilla give information about stresses and strains on the cuticle, and so
tell the insect about posture.

FIGURE 15

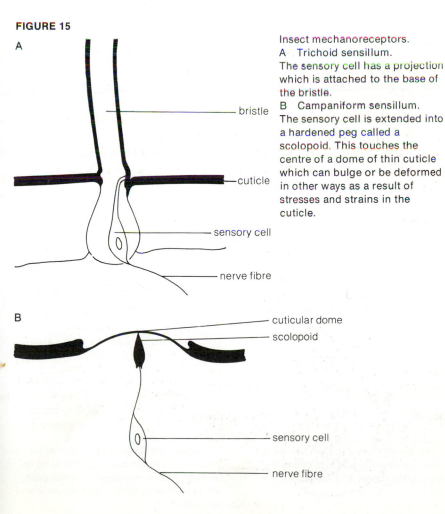

Insect mechanoreceptors.
A   Trichoid sensillum.
The sensory cell has a projection
which is attached to the base of
the bristle.
B   Campaniform sensillum.
The sensory cell is extended into
a hardened peg called a
scolopoid. This touches the
centre of a dome of thin cuticle
which can bulge or be deformed
in other ways as a result of
stresses and strains in the
cuticle.

FIGURE 16

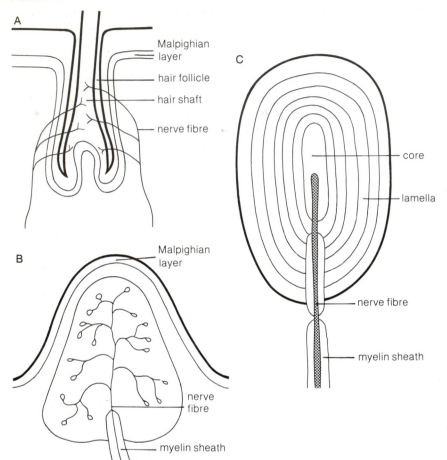

Types of mammalian skin receptors.

A   Simple nerve ending.

The nerve fibres are attached to hairs and make very efficient detectors of air movements. This can be tested by blowing very gently across the back of the hand, when very slight displacements of the hairs can be felt with air movements which cannot be detected by the hairless palm.

B   Meissner's corpuscle.

A single, highly branched nerve fibre passes between large cells within a connective tissue capsule. Meissner's corpuscles are found just under the Malpighian layer, and are sensitive to touch.

C   Pacinian corpuscle.

These are found not only in the skin, but also in joints, tendons and the mesentery of the gut where they may be particularly large, those in cat mesentery being 1 mm long and 0.5 mm across. Because of their large size, much work on the functioning of mechanoreceptors in general has been carried out on Pacinian corpuscles. The nerve ending is surrounded by lamellae of connective tissue arranged like the layers of an onion. Pressure on the lamellae deforms them and stimulates the nerve ending. Constant pressure however does not continue to deform, and so no more impulses pass along the nerve fibre – the corpuscle has adapted.

There are many simple touch and pressure receptors found scattered in mammalian skin. Some are simple nerve endings; others have nerve endings surrounded by layers of other cells. (Figure 16)

A different type of mechanoreceptor, which deals with the detection of a gravitational field, is found in nearly all the animal phyla. This type of sense organ, called a statocyst or otocyst, depends upon the mass of a small particle pressing upon the hairlike processes of certain sense cells. If the organ is moved from its normal position other cells will be stimulated. (Figure 17)

Statocysts are found with basically the same form in free swimming coelenterates, such as the medusa of *Obelia*, in some annelids, and in most of the Crustacea. Usually the statolith is a calcareous particle secreted by the epithelial lining of the statocyst. In some animals, however, it is made of grains of sand. In the lobster the statocyst is in the basal joint of the antennule, and the whole lining of the statocyst, and the sand grains are discarded when the animal moults. The lobster then replaces the sand grains by throwing sand over its head. When a lobster was allowed to moult in an aquarium containing iron filings instead of sand, it could subsequently be disorientated by a magnet held outside the tank, the magnetic attraction replacing the effect of gravity.

FIGURE 17

A

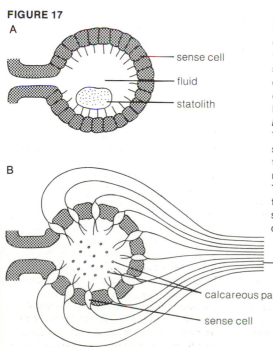

sense cell

fluid

statolith

B

nerve fibres

calcareous particles

sense cell

A   Section of a typical statocyst. Each sense cell has a displaceable hair, and a nerve fibre, and movements of the statolith produced by disorientation of the organism can be monitored.
B   Section through statocyst of *Branchiomma*, a tube worm. This has the typical statocyst structure shown in A except that the single statolith is replaced by many small calcareous particles. These fall to the lowest part of the statocyst and stimulate the sense cells there, thus giving the organism a gravitational sense.

Statocysts reach their most highly evolved form in the invertebrates in cephalopods. Each consists of a fluid filled bag, suspended in a further fluid filled cavity in the cartilage surrounding the brain. The statocysts contain the usual calcareous body which, together with the sensory cells, is called the macula. This detects a gravitational field. (Figure 18)

However angular acceleration can be detected by means of sensory cells which, together with supporting cells and large neurones, make up a ridge, called the crista, in the lining of the statocyst. The sensory hair cells have numerous projections, some of which have the typical 9 + 2 arrangement of fibrils found in cilia and which are called kinocilia. The crista ridge traces a semicircle in the horizontal plane, and then proceeds vertically to the top of the statocyst. A small flap of tissue, the cupula, is attached to each section of the crista and this, and the hair cell projections, extend into the fluid filled cavity. Movements of the animal's body, and so of the fluid, produce a drag on the cupula, shearing forces are set up in the hair cells and the neurones are stimulated.

If the cephalopod statocyst is either removed or destroyed then walking is upset, the animal tripping over its legs. Co-ordinated swimming also becomes impossible, and spiralling occurs.

Such an arrangement of gravity and movement receptors is strikingly similar to that in the vertebrate ear, and this is another example of convergent evolution in cephalopods and vertebrates.

FIGURE 18

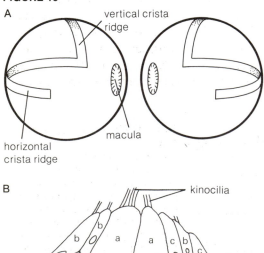

Octopus vulgaris
A Frontal diagram of statocysts to show the position of the macula and the crista ridge. The crista has sections in the horizontal and the vertical plane.
B Cross section of the crista ridge.
a – large hair cell.
b – small hair cell.
c – supporting cell.
d – large neurone.
The kinocilia project into the fluid filled cavity of the statocyst and respond to its movement (cupula not drawn).
For full description see text.

Based on Budelmann

In general, statocysts depend upon the movement of solid particles, although fluid movement is also important in cephalopods. The detection of fluid vibration assumes more importance in vertebrates. Fishes can detect, and react to, minute displacements of the surrounding water, which may be produced by the swimming movements of other fish, or water currents, or low frequency vibrations. The sense cells involved are found spaced out throughout a fluid filled canal running down each side of the fish, just under the surface. The canal opens to the water by means of pores, which are visible on the skin, and the whole system forms the lateral line. The bilateral disposition of the lateral line system enables the fish to locate the origin of water-borne vibrations. (Figure 19)

The anterior end of the lateral line system has been modified to form the ear, which can detect the direction of gravity, and also linear and angular acceleration. It was thought that the ears of fish are not particularly well adapted to dealing with the high frequency vibrations which make up sound waves, but recent research by Chapman has shown that cod have ears which are as sensitive as our own, at least over the lower range of the sound spectrum which we can hear. It is now known that a cod can hear the engine of a trawler at least five miles away, a fact which fishermen have believed for many years without scientific evidence.

Mammalian ears can carry out frequency analysis in the cochlea by means of the shearing forces set up between hair cells and the tectorial membrane, and also contain gravity and acceleration detectors.

Mechanoreceptors which can detect high frequency vibrations are also found in certain invertebrates. Insect auditory organs may be relatively simple antennal receptors depending for stimulation either on the movement of antennal hairs or of the whole antenna. When male mosquitoes are exposed to sound waves, their antennae vibrate as a

FIGURE 19

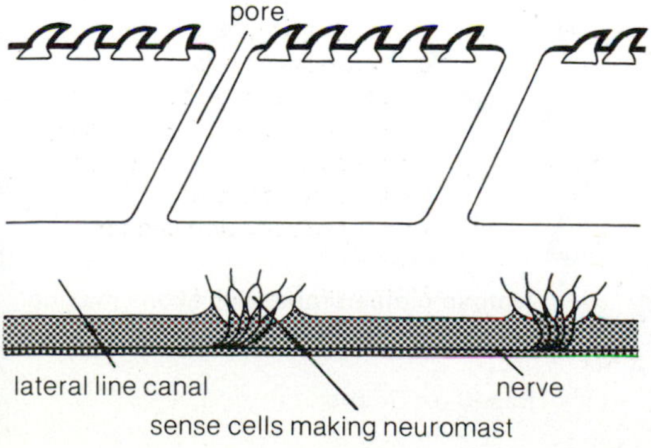

pore

lateral line canal

sense cells making neuromast

nerve

Part of the lateral line system of a fish.
The lateral line canal, filled with mucus, connects with the external water through small pores which make up the visible lateral line. Vibrations in the water stimulate the sense cells which are grouped to make the sense organs or neuromasts, and impulses pass to the brain.

whole, the males being particularly sensitive to the 500 Hertz note produced by the wing beats of the female. Similarly *Drosophila* males are attracted by a tuning fork producing the 'correct' frequency sound of about 330 Hertz.

Some insects have the ability to make relatively complicated sounds, and these have evolved more complicated auditory receptors. These usually consist of sensitive cells which touch some form of vibrating membrane or ear drum. Rather surprisingly, such efficient ears may also be found in insects which can make no sound themselves. Work by Roeder has shown that certain nocturnal moths, geometrids and noctuids, can detect ultrasonic vibrations of up to 100 000 Hertz. (Figure 20)

The ears of these moths are interesting from an experimental point of view as they contain only two sense cells in contact with a vibrating tympanic membrane. The nerve fibres from the two sense cells are relatively easy to monitor, and the range of frequencies to which the ears have been found to be sensitive covers the ultrasonic pulses given out by bats when hunting for their prey by echo-location. The moths can detect such pulses from bats a hundred feet away, and so can escape by flight, or by remaining motionless, and thus preventing the bat from receiving interesting echoes. It is not the specific frequency, but rather the pattern of pulses which is recognisable and important to the insect.

FIGURE 20

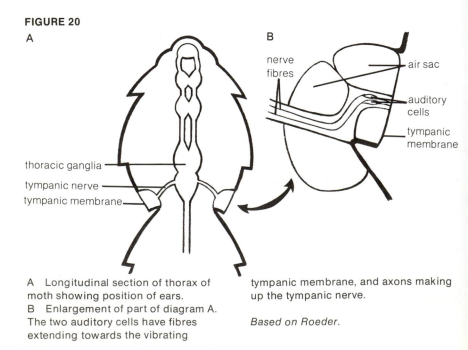

A Longitudinal section of thorax of moth showing position of ears.
B Enlargement of part of diagram A. The two auditory cells have fibres extending towards the vibrating tympanic membrane, and axons making up the tympanic nerve.

Based on Roeder.

MAGNETIC FIELD RECEPTORS

It is now becoming clear that many organisms are able to detect the earth's magnetic field, and can use such sensitivity to determine their position during migratory journeys. We shall return to this topic in a later chapter.

We can now summarise the main aspects of the reception of stimuli.

1 Sensory cells may be diffusely scattered, or may form special sense organs.

2 Sensory cells respond to particular types of stimulation, and convert the energy of the stimulus into a nerve impulse.

3 Sensory cells have the same basic pattern, consisting of a cell with either an attached nerve fibre, or a synaptic connection with a nerve cell.

4 The activity of sense cells may be monitored by recording action potentials in these afferent nerve fibres.

5 Sense cells may adapt to continued stimulation, and no longer pass impulses into their afferent nerve fibres.

4 Hormones and their effects on behaviour

Hormones are chemicals, secreted by endocrine organs, which are carried round the body usually within the blood stream and which have effects on target organs. Elaborate endocrine systems have evolved in two particular phyla. In the arthropods, hormones regulate growth, moulting, metamorphosis and the development of ovaries in the female. The responsiveness of virgin female *Drosophila melanogaster* to males depends on the age of the female. They are unresponsive for several hours after emerging from the pupa, and reach a peak of receptivity within a few days. If the corpora allata (paired ganglia above the oesophagus and the source of juvenile hormone) are removed from sexually mature female grasshoppers of the species *Gomphocerus rufus*, they will not mate with courting males, but will either fight with them or turn and flee. In other insects the sub-oesophageal ganglion appears to be important in determining behaviour. It has been suggested by Harker that the normal rhythm of nocturnal activity shown by the American cockroach, *Periplaneta americana*, is stimulated by the release of neurohumours by this ganglion, and we shall consider this more fully in Chapter 6. The most striking examples of the chemical control of behaviour in invertebrates are those in which internal hormone changes result in the production of pheromones, and we shall return to this topic later.

In chordates, and particularly in the vertebrates, hormones have a much wider range of activity and those which influence behaviour appear to do so by 'priming' the animal in some way for a particular course of action. Behaviourally potent hormones seem to be correlated with specific blocks of cells within the central nervous system, and there is evidence that they can also directly affect both receptor and effector organs. Hormones which either stimulate or are produced in the gonads have particularly important behavioural effects, and can determine the willingness of an animal to mate, how well it can maintain its position in a dominance hierarchy or how efficient a parent it will make. In female rats, for example, oestrogen levels change throughout the four day oestrus cycles, and these varying blood oestrogen levels seem to have a direct effect on sensitive cells within the hypothalamus. A high oestrogen level stimulates the female not only actively to seek copulation, but to increase her activity in other ways. A cat in oestrus will respond to the approach of a male by crouching and allowing mating, whereas she reacts aggressively if not in oestrus. Michael has shown that a female cat from which the ovaries have been surgically removed will display oestrus behaviour if oestrogen is dripped slowly into the hypothalamus. A similar replacement technique was used by Beeman to show that aggression in male mice is dependent upon the level of blood testosterone. A mouse which is castrated before becoming sexually mature does not develop aggressive behaviour, but will do so after the implantation of a pellet of testosterone.

Such androgen determined aggression is of great importance in determining and maintaining the hierarchical organisation found in many different vertebrate groups. Lincoln and his co-workers have investigated the effect of testosterone in controlling social behaviour in the red deer, *Cervus elephas*.

Red deer stags live in hierarchically arranged groups between November and August. At this time their antlers are small and are covered with soft skin called velvet, their previous antlers having been shed. The dominance hierarchy is maintained by 'low key' aggressive behaviour in which the competing males stand on their hind legs and strike out with their forefeet. The blood androgen level is low, the testes are small and do not produce spermatozoa. During this time the females live in their own groups which are also hierarchically arranged.

The mating season or 'rut' starts in September. The testes of the males now produce spermatozoa, and increase both in their size and their secretion of androgens. The resulting increased blood androgen level stimulates the growth of the antlers which erupt through the velvet, and also deepens the voice and strengthens the neck muscles. The males now go off to traditional rutting sites and challenge each other by roaring. Aggressive behaviour is no longer 'low key'; now two males will often walk side by side in a lateral threat display before rushing straight at each other and clashing antlers. The most dominant and aggressive male can collect a harem of females which have just come into oestrus, and most of them will become pregnant right away. In the rut sexual activity in the dominant males is extensive; they stop eating and may lose a considerable amount of weight. A pheromone in the urine of sexually active males gets spread over their bellies during urination and subsequently over the females during copulation and it is thought that this may indicate to the males which hinds have already been mated. However although there is an obvious correlation between androgen level and reproductive behaviour, this is not the whole story. Androgens injected into males outside the rutting time increase aggression but do not produce mating behaviour, and this is thought to be dependent on decreasing daylength also.

Many other animals show such seasonal behaviour as a result of hormone changes. In many cases endocrine glands are stimulated into action by a series of events, some external and some internal. Unlike the red deer, many seasonal animals come into reproductive behaviour in the spring, stimulated by increasing temperature or daylength. External change is detected by sense organs; impulses pass to the brain and thence to the pituitary gland; pituitary hormones then pass to the gonads. Birds, for example, are stimulated to embark upon their court-ship rituals as a result of increased daylength, received either through their eyes or more directly by their brain. In the three spined stickle-back, *Gasterosteus*, increased daylength produces, by a similar path, increased gonadal hormones which bring reproductive behaviour into action.

Although information about external change passes through the sense organs to bring about changes in hormone levels, the sense organs themselves may be affected by hormone levels. It has been found that visual sensitivity in human females varies in relation to the men-strual cycle. The ability to detect a dim test light was found to be greatest at ovulation, and least at menstruation.

Reproductive behaviour in many animals, particularly mammals and birds, is the prelude to a variable period of time in which the survival of the offspring depends on the efficiency of parental care. Nest building is common in both mammals and birds, and Zarrow and his co-workers have found that this is dependent on the amount and type of circulating reproductive hormones, at least in the domestic rabbit. Non-pregnant rabbits can be stimulated to build nests on being injected with small doses of oestrogen for eighteen days, coupled with large doses of progesterone on days two to fifteen. In the normal pregnant rabbit nest building occurs late in the gestation period when the high progesterone level drops, and it is after day fifteen when the non-pregnant rabbits make their nests.

So far we have considered only those hormones which are either produced by vertebrate gonads, or directly stimulate them. However many other endocrine glands have an effect on behaviour; hormones from both the pituitary and the thyroid are involved in maturation, and a homeostatic relationship between the two glands controls the secretion of thyroxine and therefore the basal metabolic rate. Homoiothermic (warm blooded) animals need to balance heat production against heat loss to the environment, and a variability in the basal metabolic rate is one factor which allows them to do this. The homeostatic mechanism which controls body temperature takes some time to develop in many homoiothermic animals. A new-born rat has a body temperature only about 2 °C above that of the environment, and it is twenty days before its temperature control reaches the adult condition. Bats cool down to air temperature during the day and this presumably is energetically economic, and so they need to shiver and stretch their muscles before they warm up enough to be able to fly in the evening.

An ambivalent situation arises for an animal when in a potentially dangerous position; it can either withdraw or fight. In each case its behaviour is physiologically supported by increased secretion of adrenaline by the adrenal medulla; an action further enhanced by the production of noradrenaline by the sympathetic nervous system. The rise in adrenaline and the stimulation of organs such as the heart, skeletal and respiratory muscles by the sympathetic system allow the animal to cope with a sudden emergency. However with a prolonged stressful situation the adrenal glands function in a different way. In laboratory experiments male rats were introduced singly into well established social groups, and these 'intruder' rats were usually attacked. However even though the attacks were not forceful enough to cause wounding, the 'intruders' became bedraggled, sat in the corner of the cage and many died in a few days. Selye has suggested that such animals subjected to prolonged stress undergo what he has named the 'General Adaptation Syndrome'. This seems to proceed as follows.

The alarm stage

The pituitary, activated by the brain, releases adrenocorticotrophic hormone, ACTH, which stimulates the adrenal cortex to secrete corticosteroids into the blood. These corticosteroids support the adrenaline response to the alarming situation.

The resistance stage

This is entered if stress continues. The adrenal glands enlarge and secrete more corticosteroids. A raised corticosterone level lasting over twenty-four hours has been demonstrated in laboratory mice exposed to an aggressive fighting mouse for fifteen minutes, and fighting for a short time each day results in a great enlargement of the adrenal glands. Such a continued high corticosteroid level takes the animal into the third and last stage which often leads to death.

The stage of exhaustion

With other corticosteroids adrenal androgens are secreted in increased amounts. These exert a blocking effect on the production of gonadotrophins in the pituitary, and so reproduction rates are reduced. The thymus is inhibited in its functions; antibody production falls and there is a resulting reduced resistance to infection. (Figure 21 see next page)

The 'General Adaptation Syndrome' has been suggested as an explanation of the altered reproductive patterns shown in mice living in the stressful situation of a high population density, and we shall return to this topic in the next chapter.

Although much of the work on the functioning of the 'General Adaptation Syndrome' has been based on rats and mice, there is some evidence that it also applies to other mammals. Isolation of a rhesus monkey which was a subordinate in its social group results in a decrease in ACTH production. Similarly the removal of a dominant rhesus monkey from a group leads to a decrease in ACTH production in the low ranking monkeys left behind in the group.

In man it is known that continuing auditory stimulation results in increased blood levels of corticosteroids, but so far noise has not been shown to have a contraceptive effect!

FIGURE 21

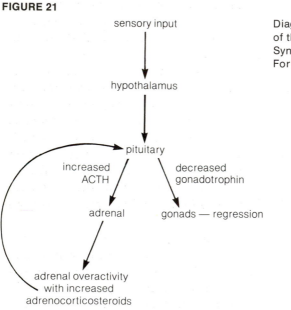

Diagram to show the operation of the General Adaptation Syndrome.
For description see text.

5 Pheromones

As we have seen in the previous chapter, hormones control many aspects of behaviour as a result of their effects on the physiology of an organism.

A highly organised animal society can be thought of, if somewhat loosely, as a type of 'super-organism' which shows an integrated structure in space and time, and it is known that many animal societies are controlled and directed by chemicals which pass from one member to another. Such chemicals were called 'ectohormones' until 1959, when they were named 'pheromones' by Karlson and Butenandt.

Such pheromones are transmitted in various ways within the animal group, and now it is recognised that they are common communication channels not only to control social organisation, but to transmit information in non-social animals. Some chemicals act on organisms of a different species, and these have been named 'allomones'. Pheromones and allomones are extremely efficient communication substances; only a few molecules need to be released and their effective range may be very great. Their evaporation sites on the producing organism may be very simple, and opening a glandular reservoir is often sufficient.

Pheromones produce two different types of response within the recipient organism. In one the response is rapid and reversible and these pheromones are said to have a 'releaser' effect. The second type is more involved; the pheromone initiates a chain of physiological events within the recipient organism which eventually equip it with a new behaviour pattern. Such a pheromone has a 'primer' effect.

RELEASER PHEROMONES

Invertebrates show numerous examples of releaser pheromones, the largest category being sex attractants. It has long been known that one way to attract male moths for trapping is to catch a female moth of the same species and to suspend her in a cage. Within a fairly short time male moths fly into the trap. The moths may be attracted from thousands of metres away by the production of minute quantities of pheromone by the female. The region of the atmosphere in which the pheromone is effective, the active space, may be a hemisphere of large radius, but is more likely to be wind blown into a region with a very long axis parallel with the wind direction, and much shorter transverse and vertical axes. At any particular spot within the active space there is no obvious diffusion gradient; so few molecules are involved that they are distributed almost uniformly. Male moths cannot therefore fly up the diffusion gradient, and it is thought that, when they are first attracted on accidentally entering the active space they proceed to fly upwind and so reach the female. The distances covered may be enormous. Marked males of the Chinese Saturnid moth, *Arctias selene*, found their way over eleven kilometres to the female. The actual quantity of pheromone is often minute; male silkworm moths will react with violent wing movements to 10^{-16}g of a pheromone named bombykol dissolved in $1\,cm^3$ petroleum ether. The male will react to this minute quantity, which must contain comparatively few molecules, even in the presence of much more concentrated contaminants. Lepidopteran pheromones are thought to be detected by the antennae and those of the males are elaborately branched and plumose. Male silk worm moths have at least ten thousand sensory hairs on each antenna, and it has been found by Schneider that only a single molecule is needed to activate a receptor cell on each hair.

In the honey bee, *Apis mellifera*, the queen produces queen substance, oxo-decenoic acid, which attracts the drones when she is on her mating flight. This substance can also act as a primer pheromone and we shall discuss this later. Pheromones are particularly important to social organisation and so it is with the social insects, termites, ants, bees and wasps, that much research has been carried out.

In the fire ant, *Solenopsis invicta*, a pheromone is produced in a posteriorly placed gland from which it passes through the extended sting of a foraging ant and on to the ground. The trail is laid down when the ant is returning to the nest from a food source, and the concentration of pheromone is proportional to the amount of food available. Other ants follow the trail from the nest to the food, and they lay down new trails as long as the food lasts. The pheromone is volatile and falls below the threshold for reception within a few minutes, thereby eliminating old, useless trails. (Figure 22)

FIGURE 22

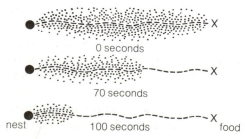

0 seconds

70 seconds

nest 100 seconds food

Scent trails left by fire ants returning to the nest from a food source.
The pheromone quickly diffuses away, and so the distance which can be marked is limited to about 50 cm.

Based on Carthy

Alarm pheromones are found in all social insects. If one honey bee worker attacks an intruder, her nest mates will move in quickly, stimulated by a pheromone released near the sting. The recent worrying invasion of South America by what are now called 'killer bees' has shown the effects of such an alarm pheromone; a person unfortunate enough to be stung by one bee is soon enveloped in a cloud of attacking, stinging workers, very often with fatal results. Many genera and species of ants produce alarm pheromones. In some cases, as in *Acanthomyops claviger*, workers run in the direction of a disturbing intruder in the nest, attracted by the gaseous diffusion of the pheromone secreted by the disturbed worker, whereas in the related ant *Lasius alienus* workers scatter and run away after disturbance.

Releaser pheromones are also found in many vertebrates. Sex attractants are widespread in fish, amphibians, birds and mammals, including the primates, and there is evidence that there are cyclical changes in the body odour of human females which act in this way. It is ironic that in this consumer society in which we live in the latter part of the twentieth century, these slowly evolved pheromones are not socially acceptable, but have to be deodorised away and replaced by a collection of necessarily expensive alternatives.

Territorial mammals may produce pheromones which act as markers at the boundaries of their territories. Male European rabbits, *Oryctolagus cuniculus*, produce such pheromones in submandibular glands, the degree of development of which depends on the rank of the individual in the dominance hierarchy. Dominant males mark out a territory for themselves and the rest of their group by 'chinning', that is rubbing the chin against the ground. Domesticated dogs follow their ancestral pattern by frequently urinating on to scent posts at the limits of their territory.

Such releaser pheromones which act as sex attractants, territory markers or dominance signals produce the relatively simple response of attraction or repulsion in the recipient. Primer pheromones have a much more involved, and less easily elucidated action.

PRIMER PHEROMONES

Primer pheromones are known to be important in both invertebrate and vertebrate groups.

The male locust of the species *Schistocerca gregaria* matures more slowly if kept alone than if it is with other males. However cotton wool pads soaked in an ether extract of mature males make a suitable substitute for the male companions.

In the honey bee the basic organisation and caste system are partly controlled by queen substance, oxo-decenoic acid, which we have already mentioned in its role as a sex attractant and so as a releaser pheromone. The queen bee produces the substance in her mandibular glands and then smears it over herself in her grooming activities. She is usually surrounded by workers which lick her and so the pheromone enters the food exchange system. This food exchange system of regurgitation and secondary feeding, called trophallaxis, is a rapid and efficient means for materials to pass from one worker to another. In one experiment six foraging bees were allowed to feed on honey containing radio-active phosphorus, and within twenty-four hours sixty percent of a colony of twenty-five thousand bees had become radio-active. As long as the queen substance passes through this food exchange system it controls the behaviour of the workers by ensuring that they make small, regularly shaped worker cells. If the queen substance stops flowing, or is severely reduced in quantity, then the workers make larger queen cells. Such a situation can be achieved experimentally by removing the queen from a colony, or by separating her from the workers by a gauze screen of sufficient thickness to stop them touching her. (Figure 23) In natural conditions the production of queen substance drops as the swarming season approaches and then the building of queen cells will follow. Eggs laid into these cells will develop into larvae which are continually fed on a special rich food called royal jelly, which results in fast growth and earlier metamorphosis into new queens.

In vertebrates primer pheromone activity has been found to be important in some animals in controlling reproduction. The laboratory mouse, *Mus musculus*, has been found to be sensitive to the presence of

FIGURE 23

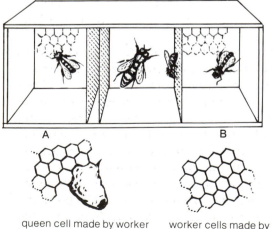

queen cell made by worker in section **A**

worker cells made by workers in section **B**

Experiment to show the importance of queen substance in the honey bee.
The queen in the centre compartment is attended by some workers, but is separated from the workers in the left section A by two gauze screens. These workers can touch neither the queen nor her attendant workers, and within forty-eight hours they have built a queen cell. (below)
The workers in the right section B can touch the queen or her attendants through the single gauze screen; they go on building worker cells.

Based on Butler.

other mice in many ways. Bruce found that exposure of a recently impregnated female to a different male from her mate results in a failure of implantation of the blastocyst and a return of the female to oestrus. She is then willing to mate with the new male, and so the pheromone he produces has been useful to him in ensuring that she will produce his offspring, and not those of the earlier male.

If four or more female mice are living together in the absence of a male, then oestrus is suppressed and the mice may have pseudopregnancies. This is called the Lee-Boot effect. If a group of such females is exposed to a male, then they will all reach oestrus within three or four days – the Whitten effect. The presence of other mice can produce an enlargement of the adrenal glands and a reduction in reproductive capacity, and this is a partial explanation of the stress syndrome mentioned in the previous chapter. The pheromones involved in these effects have not yet been chemically identified but it is thought that there are probably three: an oestrus inhibitor, an oestrus inducer and an adrenocortical stimulator.

A rather similar synchronisation of reproductive cycles has been reported by McClintock. It has been found that groups of young women living communally in Halls of Residence develop a synchrony of their menstrual cycles, but, as yet, this has not proved to be pheromonal.

From what we have said, it is obvious that chemical communication has many advantages. Pheromones can travel as well in the dark as in daylight, and they are not impeded by many obstacles. The molecules used are small and are easily synthesised and, although they need be made only in small quantities, they have an enormous active space. Some of the less volatile pheromones may go on functioning as territory markers for a long time. However as pheromones depend on the surrounding environment for their transmission, there could be a long delay between the signal and the response.

One of the less well considered aspects of our present concern about environmental pollution is the possible interference of chemical pollution with such an efficient means of communication. In the bullhead catfish, for example, the dominance order is organised and maintained by the production and reception of pheromones. Chemical pollution of the water interferes with this and the result is continual fighting. A very low concentration of 0.8 parts per billion of the sea water soluble fraction of kerosine interferes with the ability of the marine snail *Nassarius obsoletus* to locate its food, and it is likely that it would have the same effect on the reception of water-borne pheromones. The pollution may not even need to be measurable; minimal chemical alteration of the atmospheric gases or the oceans could reduce a highly evolved and efficient information system to uselessness.

6 Biological rhythms

It is becoming apparent that one of the fundamental characteristics of living organisms is their capacity somehow to measure the passage of time. The environmental cues used are varied, and the reception and physiological effects of changes in the environment differ from one species to another. Rhythmical control of metabolism and behaviour are found in both unicellular and multicellular organisms; in some higher organisms there is evidence of several different timing systems running alongside each other in one individual. The periodic cues present in the environment result from the relative positions of the earth, the moon and the sun. The earth's daily rotation produces periods of light and darkness; the tilt of the earth's axis alters such periods of light and darkness into a 'warm, long day, short night/cold, short day, long night' rhythm as the earth moves in its yearly orbit around the sun. Superimposed on these are the gravitational effects the moon has on the oceans, producing tides, and the alternation of spring and neap tides resulting from the relative positions of the sun, the earth and the moon. As these environmental conditions have remained relatively fixed in their periodicity during the time in which organisms have been evolving on earth, it would be surprising if they had not shown some adaptation to them.

CIRCADIAN RHYTHMS

A circadian rhythm is a cyclical variation in the intensity of a physiological process or behaviour pattern with a periodicity of about twenty-four hours (circa – about, dies – a day). It may be endogenous, that is, it originates within the organism, and then we may speak of it as a biological clock. Sometimes the rhythm is exogenous and is imposed directly on the organism by the daily periodicity of an external factor. Endogenous rhythms will persist even if the external conditions are kept constant; exogenous rhythms will not.

In the eighteenth century investigators studied the movement of plant leaflets over a twenty-four hour period and demonstrated an endogenous rhythm which was not altered by a change in the external light. Since then a large number of animals and plants have been shown to have persistent twenty-four hour cycles of activity. In some cases maximum activity is shown during the hours of darkness, (nocturnal organisms); in others more activity occurs in the light (diurnal organisms). Anyone who has kept a pet hamster in a cage with a squeaky running wheel will be only too aware that the dark hours are the times of greatest activity. A similar pattern of running activity is seen in cockroaches and this has been associated with the sub-oesophageal ganglion. (Figure 24)

Cockroaches begin to move about when it gets dark. In one experiment a cockroach which had been kept in constant light and showed no sign of an activity rhythm, was surgically attached to one which had been kept in a twelve-hour light/twelve-hour darkness cycle and which had a clear rhythmic pattern. The pair were connected, back to back, in such a way that one could walk about carrying the other one, and in this experiment the arhythmic cockroach was the one underneath. In conditions of constant light the walking, previously arhythmic, cockroach began following a twenty-four hour rhythm, the peak of which followed the time setting for the uppermost, rhythmic cockroach. This, and other parabiosis experiments where two organisms were joined together, suggested that a hormone is involved in rhythmic activity, and Harker thinks that this is a neuro-humour secreted by the sub-oesophageal ganglion. At present there is much conflicting evidence about the importance of the sub-oesophageal ganglion in controlling rhythmic activity in insects. It may be that the sub-oesophageal ganglion is just one of many different clocks.

A nocturnal activity pattern has also been demonstrated in the larvae of the nematode, *Wurchereria bancrofti*, which is parasitic in man. In its adult stage the nematode causes elephantiasis and the larvae (microfilariae) are transmitted from one person to another by the

FIGURE 24

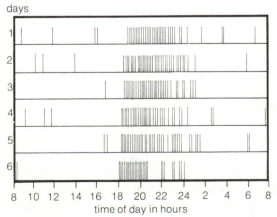

days

time of day in hours

Activity record of a cockroach kept in constant darkness after a circadian rhythm had been established.

During the six days in constant darkness this particular cockroach maintained a circadian rhythm with a period of just less than twenty-four hours.

Based on Harker.

mosquito *Culex fatigans*. Samples of blood taken during the day from someone known to be infected with the larvae will rarely show their presence, whereas a peripheral blood sample taken at night time will contain large numbers of these microscopic larvae. Such a periodicity is an adaptation to the nocturnal blood sucking behaviour shown by the mosquito vector. However the periodicity can be altered by a change in the sleeping habits of the patient. (Figure 25)

As we see, even though endogenous circadian rhythms will persist in the absence of the usual environmental cues, they may be affected by several external factors such as the intensity and quality of the light, or variations in temperature, and can then be advanced or retarded in phase. Investigations into endogenous rhythms in man in which volunteers spent periods of time in caves without the usual light/dark cues, or any form of external clock, have shown that the biological clock may persist in its twenty-four hour rhythm, or may re-establish itself for a longer or shorter period. The Frenchman, Michel Siffre spent a long period of time in a cave 375 feet under the Alpes Maritime, and his internal clock re-established itself at longer than twenty-four hours. When he emerged from the cave on September 14 after sixty-two days, his personal internal calendar told him, erroneously, that it was August 20.

Many human processes show a circadian rhythm; mitosis within the epidermis takes place at higher rates at night; body temperature and heart rate are highest in daytime; oxygen consumption and carbon dioxide production are also higher during day time. Urine production falls during the night hours, and so one does not have one's sleep disturbed by the sensation of a full bladder. (Figure 26)

Alcohol is oxidised more slowly and therefore produces a greater effect between 2 am and noon – a fact that might be worth considering if you want to organise a party, with drinks, as cheaply as possible, with the added advantage that the guests would be too sleepy to drink much anyway!

Tolerance of pain is highest at midnight. That might seem to be the ideal time to have a dental appointment, but for the fact that the muscular skill and mental alertness of the dentist would then be at their lowest level.

Normally, as can be seen in figure 26, these physiological processes are in phase with each other, but under abnormal circumstances they may become desynchronised. In one investigation volunteers spent a period of time during the Arctic summer in Spitsbergen, where there is little difference in light intensity from day to night. The volunteers used watches which made one full turn of the hour hand in 10.5, 11 or 13.5 hours, and so they were based on a 21, 22 or 27 hour day.

FIGURE 25

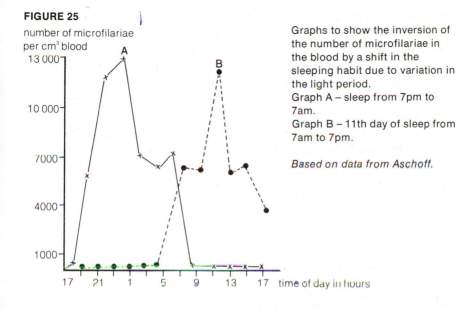

number of microfilariae per cm³ blood

Graphs to show the inversion of the number of microfilariae in the blood by a shift in the sleeping habit due to variation in the light period.
Graph A – sleep from 7pm to 7am.
Graph B – 11th day of sleep from 7am to 7pm.

Based on data from Aschoff.

FIGURE 26

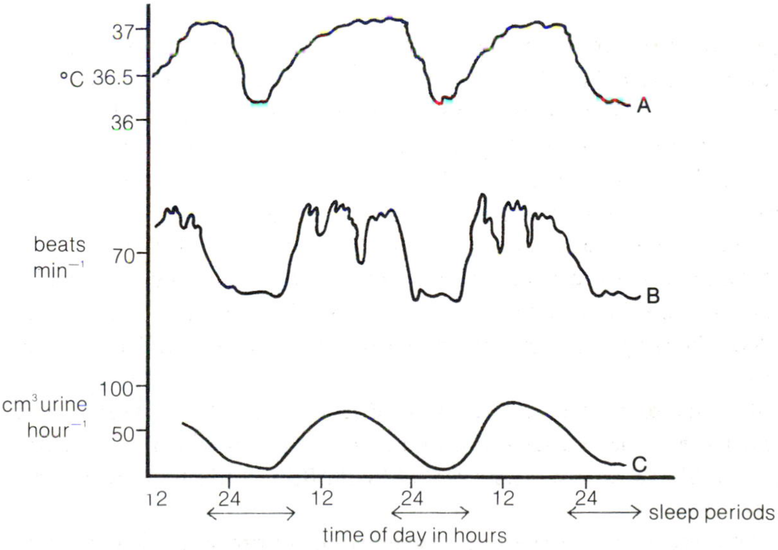

Typical graphs showing circadian variation in human physiological processes.
Graph A – body temperature.
Graph B – heart rate.
Graph C – urine production.

The different physiological processes being investigated (excretion of water and potassium, and body temperature) altered at different rates to the changed daily rhythms of the volunteers. Potassium excretion continued to follow a twenty-four hour periodicity, unlike the other processes, and so there was a disturbance of the normal phase relationships, with very unpleasant results for some of the volunteers.

A circadian rhythm is also shown in the ability to perform physical and mental tasks, the poorest capability being shown at night time. This highlights the difficulty experienced by some people when on shift work, in which the external environmental cues are oppposite in phase to the internal rhythm. A similar, and potentially more dangerous, situation arises for the crew of modern aircraft who, by traversing time zones, are exposed to days which may be artificially shortened or lengthened.

An endogenous rhythm running on a twenty-four hour period is an adaptation to the environmental conditions in which organisms have evolved. This has been capitalised upon by many organisms which use external cues, together with their internal clocks, in order to navigate over large or small distances. For a sun compass to be effective the relative movement of the sun across the sky must be measured against an internal standard of time, otherwise large, and potentially fatal, navigational errors will result. Many investigators have been able to show that such a situation occurs.

In one series of experiments carried out by Brun, ants which had found food and were returning to the nest were covered, in situ, with a light proof box which was left there for several hours. The sun meanwhile had changed its position in the sky. The box was then removed and the ant continued on its way. If the investigation was carried out on ants of the species Formica rufa, it was found that they had measured the elapsed time and therefore 'knew' that the sun had altered its position in the sky; they compensated for this and took the correct path to the nest. However if the ants were of the different species, Lasius niger, they kept their original orientation to the sun, travelled in the wrong direction and did not reach the nest. (Figure 27)

Hoffmann trained starlings to fly in a particular compass direction to a food source some distance away. He then exposed the birds to an artificial light/dark cycle which was either several hours ahead or behind the natural situation. When tested in normal conditions after several days in these altered times, the birds flew in a direction which deviated from the trained direction in a mathematically predictable way, depending on the time shift of their internal cycles. (Figure 28)

We shall return to the subject of orientation and navigation in a later chapter.

FIGURE 27

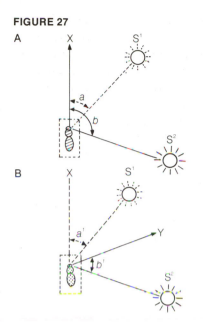

Brun's experiments with ants.
In each diagram S¹ is the original, and S² the eventual position of the sun, and X is the position of the nest. The ant is shown covered by the light proof box (dotted line)
Diagram A   experiment with *Formica rufa.*
The ant takes account of the sun's movement, and angle *b* is appropriately larger than angle *a*.
Diagram B   experiment with *Lasius niger.*
The ant does not measure elapsed time and keeps the original orientation to the sun, angle *b¹* = angle *a¹*. It therefore moves towards Y and not towards the real position of the nest, X.

FIGURE 28

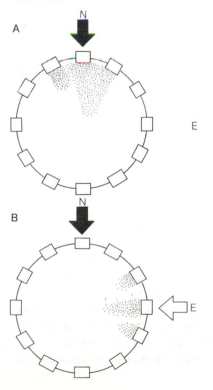

Hoffmann's experiments with starlings.
A   The shaded areas indicate the feeding responses of a particular starling which had been trained to feed at noon from the most northerly of twelve boxes arranged in a circle. The bird was then removed from its outdoor cage and was kept inside with artificially altered light/dark cycles. 'Noon' inside was really 6pm outside.
B   After two weeks in the altered cycle the starling was returned to its outdoor cage. Now the bird flew to the most easterly box, its internal clock telling it that at noon it needed to fly directly away from the sun. It was therefore 90° out, or one quarter of the sun's daily cycle.

TIDAL RHYTHMS

Many marine organisms show synchronisation of their behaviour with the movement of the tides. Some shore organisms such as the green flatworm, *Convoluta*, rise to the surface of the sand when it is covered by water and retreat to lower regions of the sand when it dries out. Others follow a reversed pattern. The diatom *Hantzschia virgata* moves to the surface of the sand to photosynthesise while the tide is out, and returns to below the surface just before the tide comes in.

Fiddler crabs, *Uca* species, also normally emerge from their burrows at low tides to eat any detritus available on the surface, and retreat when water again covers the sand. Laboratory investigations in which single crabs were placed in knife edge actographs showed that the tidal rhythm of activity continued for up to five weeks in some species, even in the constant conditions of an incubator. In other species the rhythm damped down rather more quickly, although it could be maintained for a longer period if the crab were immersed in sea water at intervals. In natural conditions small populations of fiddler crabs may become established along the margins of pools which are not subject to tides, and then the tidal rhythm is lost, and a circadian rhythm is shown.

There are two tides per lunar day, that is the interval between two successive moonrises, and in some tidal organisms a bimodal tidal rhythm which depends on the 24.8 hour lunar day is superimposed upon a 24 hour circadian rhythm. Activity graphs of these organisms are not obviously periodic. Investigations by Naylor into activity in crabs showed that the shore crab, *Carcinus maenas*, from England shows such an apparently aperiodic pattern, but *Carcinus mediterraneus* from the Bay of Naples shows a very clear circadian rhythm. It is significant that tidal change in the Bay of Naples is extremely small.

LUNAR RHYTHMS

Tidal rhythms are related to the length of the lunar day, but tidal rhythms corresponding to the 28.5 day cycle of the moon's movement around the earth are also shown by several marine organisms.

The palolo worm of the Pacific and Atlantic oceans reproduces only during the neap tides of the last quarter moon in October and November. The palolo is a polychaete worm which reproduces by the breaking away of the sexual posterior part of the adult, the rest of which remains hidden within a rock. The sexual pieces rise to the surface in millions, and there both eggs and sperm are liberated in reasonably close proximity, thereby increasing the chance of fertilisation. Such swarming is well known to the Samoan islanders who eat the palolo with enjoyment, and can catch them in large quantities at this time.

The grunion fish, *Leuresthes tenuis*, of the Californian coast is washed ashore by a spring tide, and there it deposits its eggs or sperm before being swept back to sea. The fertilised eggs develop in the moist, warm sand, but are not covered again by water until the next spring tide a fortnight later. By then the young fish have developed enough to leave the eggs and be washed out to the open sea.

Lunar rhythms have also been described with mussels, sea urchins and the brown alga *Dictyota dichotoma*, which liberates its gametes at certain phases of the moon. Even terrestrial animals can show lunar periodicity. The granary weevil *Calandra granaria* has cycles of photo-tactic responsiveness which correspond to the lunar phases, and the numbers of the moth *Heliothis zea*, the bollworm, caught in light traps also show rhythmic increases and decreases corresponding to the lunar phases. For millennia man worshipped a Moon goddess, who was thought to preside over the tides, the fertility of his crops and animals, and also of course, the fertility of women.

ANNUAL RHYTHMS

As we have already seen, many organisms have an inbuilt biological clock which monitors the passage of time throughout the day. The daily alternation between the hours of daylight and of darkness must alter in their relative lengths throughout the year. A reaction to altered day-length is called photoperiodism, and although the phenomenon was first investigated in relation to flowering in plants, it is now known that photoperiodic mechanisms also occur in many animals as we have already mentioned for red deer and the three spined stickleback.

Rowan in the nineteen twenties first suggested that increased daylength was responsible for the reproductive and migratory behaviour in birds, and he found that an artificial increase in the daily light period in Autumn could induce gonad enlargement and the impulse to fly North in many birds which normally migrate northward in the spring. Since then photoperiodism has been investigated in many birds. It was found in the Japanese quail, for example, that reproductive behaviour could be induced at the wrong season if the daylength was kept above nine hours. Further experiments showed that the important factor was the timing of two consecutive light periods, which had to be about fourteen hours apart. The birds would breed at any season even if they received a total daily light exposure of thirty minutes only, if this were given as two fifteen minute periods, fourteen hours apart. The first light period seems to set the biological clock; the second initiates the secretion of releasing factors by the hypothalamus which stimulate the production of gonadotrophins by the anterior lobe of the pituitary.

Diapause in insects is also related to daylength. In various species of aphids reproductive cycles and seasonal migration can be affected by artificially altering the daylength.

The sensory and neural mechanisms needed for this type of daylength measurement have not yet been fully elucidated in animals. It appears that many different pigments may be involved in different species, and so the story is much more complicated than in plants, where the red/far red phytochrome system appears to be the usual mechanism.

7 Innate behaviour

As we have seen in earlier chapters, both receptors and nervous systems show a vast range of complexity from the very simple organelles and cytoplasmic transmission found in protists to the highly integrated circuitry of higher vertebrates. The simpler the sense organ, the smaller the amount of information which can be fed into the circuit. An increased number of connecting or internuncial neurones within the transmission system will provide more potential pathways, and so more variable behaviour will be possible.

In simple organisms a particular type and intensity of stimulation will always evoke the same response; *Euglena* will move towards unilateral light, and *Paramecium* will gather in a particular acidity level. Such behaviour is stereotyped as it is an unvarying response to the stimulus. The complementarity of the stimulus and the response depends upon the inherited characteristics of the transmission system, whether it is intracellular as in protists or within a nervous system, and so such stereotyped behaviour is innate.

Innate behaviour has been investigated by many different workers and this has led to the historic division into three classes of behaviour: reflexes – as studied by Pavlov, Watson and others; orientation behaviour – analysed by Fraenkel and Gunn; instinctive behaviour, or complex fixed action patterns, in the study of which ethologists such as Tinbergen have been predominant.

REFLEXES

A reflex action is a usually brief automatic response in an effector brought about by the transmission of impulses from a receptor.

The simplest form of reflex action requires only two nerve cells; a sensory neurone which is initially stimulated and a motor neurone with which it makes a synaptic connection. This is the level of organisation shown in the intra-segmental reflexes of the earthworm, but even in man such a simple system is found in the two-neurone knee-jerk reflex. (Figure 29) In most cases the sensory and motor neurones are linked by one or more connecting or internuncial neurones. These connecting neurones can spread the response obtained, and so in the earthworm adjacent segments may respond to stimulation by means of inter-segmental reflexes. In man the relatively simple reflex action of removing one's finger from a sharp object may, and probably will, also involve

FIGURE 29

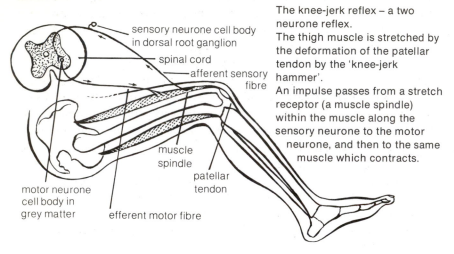

sensory neurone cell body in dorsal root ganglion

spinal cord

afferent sensory fibre

muscle spindle

patellar tendon

motor neurone cell body in grey matter

efferent motor fibre

The knee-jerk reflex – a two neurone reflex.
The thigh muscle is stretched by the deformation of the patellar tendon by the 'knee-jerk hammer'.
An impulse passes from a stretch receptor (a muscle spindle) within the muscle along the sensory neurone to the motor neurone, and then to the same muscle which contracts.

responses of the leg muscles, the other arm, and the diaphragm and intercostal muscles producing a cry. Impulses pass from the shoulder level segments of the spinal cord, through nerve fibres in the white matter, to motor neurones at other segmental levels. At the same time impulses pass to the brain, and, although this does not control and organise the response, it is useful that it can register what has happened.

Even though the brain is not the instigator of such a reflex action there are circumstances in which the behaviour pattern can be consciously modified. One's reaction to receiving an injection in the buttock is likely to be quite different from that produced by unexpectedly sitting on a drawing pin. In the first case anticipation is important, and the brain is acting as an inhibitor preventing what would be the expected reflex pattern of leaping in the air.

Reflexes such as these which are rapid and basically protective – phasic reflexes, may be compared with the slow, long lasting postural reflexes – tonic reflexes. These usually involve effectors innervated at all levels of the spinal cord. Righting reflexes, for example, require a large number of muscles in various parts of the body linked with the eyes, the ears and the brain, and the co-ordinated patterns of contraction and relaxation of antagonistic muscles needed for locomotion show a similar widespread involvement of effectors.

ORIENTATION BEHAVIOUR

The orientation of an organism means its change of position in relation to an external stimulus. This being so, it is obvious that many reflexes could be described as examples of orientation behaviour. Similarly one can describe some examples of orientation behaviour in terms of a series of reflex acts. The difference is mainly one of degree. Phasic reflexes are short lived and limited in their effects, and although tonic reflexes last much longer they are primarily concerned with information from proprioceptors within the organism.

Orientation behaviour may be readily seen in organisms which are suddenly subjected to potentially harmful stimulation. Turning over a large stone when gardening will often expose large numbers of wood-lice which suddenly jerk out of their apparent stupor and start moving at random. Digging and turning over the soil will place earthworms on the surface, a fact utilised by birds which follow the plough. However the birds need to be quick; the earthworms very rapidly move into deeper soil and comparative safety. These two examples of orientation behaviour differ in a fundamental way. In the first, stimulation produces what appears to be random movement, whereas the earthworm carries out a directed response. The first is an example of a kinesis, and the second of a taxis.

Kineses

A kinesis is a behaviour pattern in which an animal responds to an alteration in stimulus intensity by changing its activity level. The movements produced are random, and altering the stimulus intensity can have two different effects. In the first, orthokinesis, the actual rate of movement alters. Klinokinesis involves an alteration in the frequency of turning carried out by the organism in its random movements.

In the example of the woodlice stimulated into activity by a change in their surroundings, one could hypothesise that the sudden exposure to drier air is an important factor. Such a hypothesis can be tested by placing the animals in an apparatus called a choice chamber in which a humidity gradient can be produced. (Figure 30)

FIGURE 30

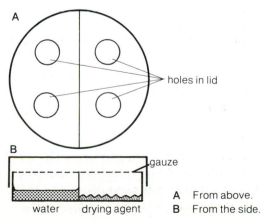

A From above.
B From the side.

A simple choice chamber. A transparent dish is divided into two layers by a sheet of gauze. Beneath the gauze the chamber is divided into sections to accommodate substances which produce a humidity gradient above the gauze. After setting up the holes in the lid are covered with sticky tape, and the apparatus is left for 20 minutes for the humidity to stabilise. The sticky tape is then momentarily removed to allow small animals such as woodlice to be introduced through the holes.

If the woodlice are originally fairly evenly distributed over the gauze by being introduced through the holes in the lid, the holes then being covered with sticky tape, it soon becomes obvious that those animals which are in the humid area are motionless or moving slowly, whereas those in the dry area are walking more quickly. Dryness appears to produce the reflex activity of walking, and as the animals move more quickly in the dry areas, at any particular time more will be found over the water in the choice chamber. Such an orthokinetic reaction will result in an aggregation of woodlice in the damp region, and this is aided by a klinokinetic alteration in their turning rate. When woodlice move from damp into dry air their rate of turning increases. By chance this can bring them back into humid conditions and this, coupled with slowing down, is usually enough to keep them all in humid conditions.

A choice chamber such as this can be used to investigate orientation responses to light and heat also, although there may be experimental problems. If a temperature gradient is set up with the dish hot at one end and cold at the other, there will also be a gradient of relative humidity. Similarly a gradient of light intensity may also be a temperature gradient. It is also necessary to turn the apparatus regularly to cancel out the effects of external factors such as unilateral light from the laboratory window.

As we have said, choice chambers can be used to observe the responses of a group of animals to graduated stimuli and here the number of animals in each area is regularly counted. A chamber can also be used with a single animal, the observer continuously watching its movements and copying them onto paper. Such a drawing will not only show preferred conditions; it will also show klinokinetic responses.

Taxes

A taxis is a movement that is orientated in relation to the direction of a stimulus. There are three basic types of taxes which are dependent upon the particular sensory system of the organism.

In the first type, klinotaxis, there is a comparison between the strength of stimulation at one instant and at the instant preceding it. This is usually what happens if an organism has either a single sense organ for the particular type of stimulus or two organs which are very close together. By alternately placing its anterior end to the left and to the right, a blowfly maggot will crawl, in an approximately straight line, away from a source of light. When it has its anterior end to the left, its left receptor will be stimulated, and this causes the maggot to swing to the right. This leads to stimulation of the right receptor and so the animal now swings to the left. Klinotaxis involves a short term memory.

Tropotaxis results from a simultaneous comparison of the stimulus intensity received by bilaterally symmetrical sense organs. The animal can move either towards or away from the stimulus as long as it keeps both receptors equally stimulated. Tropotaxis can be demonstrated in two main ways.

1 If the animal is unilaterally deprived of a receptor, then it will constantly turn to one side in a diffuse field of stimulation. So an animal which would normally move away from light by tropotaxis, and which has one eye covered, will move in circles constantly turning to its blind side when subjected to light from above.

2 If two stimuli are presented then the animal will move on a path which lies between them. This however can also be shown by klinotaxis, and we return to this point later.

As we see, in tropotaxis the animal moves towards or away from the stimulus, or takes a path which is a resultant of the two stimulus intensities. Simultaneous comparison of the intensity of stimulation is the important characteristic of tropotaxis. However such simultaneous comparison is also important in the dorsal light reaction in which the animal moves at right angles to the stimulus. Aquatic animals will swim in their normal horizontal position as long as light comes from above. If the position of the light is altered, then they change their orientation accordingly. Some ethologists separate the dorsal light reaction from tropotaxis because the animal does not move towards or away from the stimulus. Others feel that orientation which balances sensory stimulation, and in which unilateral blinding results in spiralling movements, is fundamentally a tropotaxis.

A rather more complicated technique is found in telotaxis. Here the animal orients towards one source of stimulation and ignores any others. This means that the influence of the ignored stimulus must be inhibited in some way. The animal keeps one particular region of the sense organ continually fixated on the chosen stimulus. The compound eyes of insects are well adapted for such a mechanism. Certain ommatidia produce a greater turning response than others, those facing backwards eliciting more violent turning to a light behind the animal. The ommatidia facing forward at the front of the eye produce no turning at all when stimulated, and once the insect has turned far enough for this section to be stimulated, it will keep moving in a straight line.

In telotaxis, orientation is directly towards or away from a stimulus to the exclusion of others. A variation of this is found where animals can move at a constant angle to a source of stimulation, as in the light compass reaction shown by many insects. Here sunlight is fixated on certain ommatidia and so the insect can use the position of the sun as a bearing for navigation. Such a reaction is called menotaxis.

In these examples the stimulus is very simple, but in some cases stimulation may be complex. A dragonfly will orient towards its prey in what appears to be telotaxis, but the actual visual pattern produced by the prey may become important by learning. The solitary hunting wasp, *Philanthus triangulum*, orients to its nest firstly by the light compass reaction, but eventually by recognising a learned pattern of landmarks. Reaction to such a learned pattern of configurational stimuli is called pharotaxis; the animal however responds in a telotactic way by ignoring other stimuli.

The three basic types of taxes can be distinguished from each other by the simple experiment which we have already mentioned using two sources of stimulation, such as two lights. (Figure 31)

Two equal intensity lights placed in front of the experimental animal will induce movement towards or away from them, depending on whether the animal is photopositive or photonegative. Animals which show klinotaxis or tropotaxis will move on a path equidistant from both lights, the klinotactic animal showing regular oscillation about the line. If one light is increased in intensity, then the path will be nearer to the weaker light, as it is here that the stimulus intensity will be equal. A telotactic animal will move towards one light and will ignore the other.

FIGURE 31

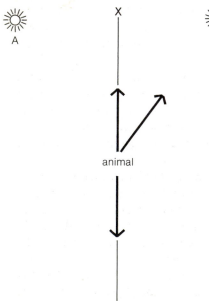

A two light experiment. Given two lights of equal intensity, A and B, the organism may move along the path XY, that is along a path equidistant from the lights. This shows klinotaxis or tropotaxis. Some organisms however can ignore one light and move to the other one by means of a telotactic response.

Each of these types of taxes may also be named according to the stimulus, and whether the organism moves towards or away from it. So we have positive phototaxis in *Euglena* resulting in it moving towards the light, and negative phototaxis in the blowfly maggot. In each case the organism reaches the optimum situation; *Euglena* in enough light for photosynthesis, and the blowfly maggot in the dark, inside or underneath the dead food organism, and therefore protected from both predators and desiccation.

Each of these two classes of innate behaviour is concerned with relatively simple actions which can be analysed and described fairly easily. The next class is much more complex.

INSTINCTIVE BEHAVIOUR

'Instinct' is a term which has been freely used by amateur naturalists to cover what they see as the mysterious cleverness of nature in ensuring that each organism knows both its place and its role in the great scheme of things. Mysteriousness was important, and to label a particular behaviour pattern an instinct was explanation enough. Today ethologists have gone far in removing the sterility of such an outlook.

Instinctive behaviour can be defined as species specific (that is, found in all members of a particular species), innate (unlearned) and adaptive, but these properties cannot be looked upon as completely rigid. Ethologists now see such innate behaviour as a complex interaction of internal and external conditions. The behaviour pattern appears, as if ready made, at its first performance; a situation which is very necessary in animals with a short life span and little or no parental care. In many insects, for example, the adult emerges from the pupa and has then to carry out a complicated pattern of behaviour which may include nest building, a courtship ritual, and provisioning the nest with the right sort of food for the new larva. All of this must be done in the proper sequence, and often within the space of a few weeks. There is no time for trial and error and often there are no other animals of the same species available to act as models.

The leaf cutter bee, *Megachile*, builds its tunnel shaped nest in rotting wood, and then proceeds to cut small circles out of particular leaves. These leaf pieces are used to line the walls of the tunnel and to make a lid. A mixture of pollen and honey is placed, with a single egg, in a cell which is then capped. Other cells are made alongside and so the nest is filled. The solitary wasp, *Ammophila campestris*, also provisions its nest for the larva. In this case a caterpillar is stung in various segments, and the wasp poison acts on the nervous system of the caterpillar producing degeneration of all the ganglia, but allowing the heart to continue beating. The nest is made at the bottom of a long, vertical tunnel in the ground, which is sealed at the opening by pebbles. When the immobilised caterpillar has been dragged into the nest, a single egg is laid on it. The female then leaves the nest, replacing the pebbles at the opening. The bee and the wasp seem to display rather similar behaviour patterns. In each case a tunnel is made, the cell is provisioned and a single egg is laid there. There is, however, a difference in the rigidity of the behaviour pattern. *Ammophila* may be working on two or three nests at the same time, unlike *Megachile* which makes only one, and it can switch from an 'early' act to a 'late' act without difficulty, but if the nest of a leaf cutting bee is partially destroyed the bee continues in its rigid sequence as if nothing has happened.

Both of these patterns can be called instincts; the differences depend on the relative importance of external and internal stimulation.

In many instinctive behaviour patterns there must be an element of learning. Even the rigidly determined leaf cutter bee must learn the position of its nest so that it can return to it with its leaf circles, and *Ammophila* must remember the positions of its two or three nests.

In higher organisms it becomes more and more difficult to separate the truly innate behaviour from its learned components. A bird reared in isolation will be able to perform the species specific song; the song, however, will not usually be quite as elaborate as that of birds which can copy the finer points from other birds. The work of Harlow on isolation of baby rhesus monkeys has shown that even such fundamental behaviour patterns as mating can be seriously affected by the absence of models from which the young animals can learn.

While keeping these reservations about instincts in mind, it is possible to analyse such behaviour into various stages.

To begin with, the animal is motivated by some internal change. This may be relatively simple like hunger, or may be a complicated change in hormone balance produced by an external stimulus such as changing daylength. This internal change stimulates the animal to carry out what is sometimes called appetitive behaviour in which it may move around in what appears to be a random way, or the movements may look purposeful. Learning and experience may play a great part during this stage. A hungry animal will become more efficient at searching out food as its experience of the habits of its prey increases. At some time during this behaviour the animal may encounter a particular stimulus which will trigger off the complete instinctive act.

Such a stimulus is known as a sign stimulus; sign stimuli which elicit behaviour in members of the same species are called releasers. Obviously at any time an animal is subjected to a wide array of sensory stimulation. Even if one considers only that received by one type of receptor such as eyes, there is still a vast amount of information being fed into the animal. At any time the animal sees a whole picture or pattern, and such a complete picture has been called a *gestalt* by one school of psychologists. Out of this complicated *gestalt* one section will act as the important signal, although in most cases it will not elicit a response if presented in isolation from the background pattern. The animal must therefore be able to select the 'right' bit of information from the background pattern and to react to it. (Figure 32)

The effectiveness of a particular stimulus in eliciting a behaviour pattern can be assessed in various ways.

Sometimes direct observation gives a good clue. Large white butterfles, *Pieris brassica*, flutter around blue flowers, but will also flutter about a blue book, and this suggests that it is the 'blueness', rather than the scent, which is important.

Surgical interference such as the severance of the olfactory nerves of a bird, or the amputation of the antennae of an insect, may show that olfactory stimuli are important in feeding behaviour.

A common experimental technique involves the presentation of models to the experimental animal. The models can be altered in a systematic way, and their effects on behaviour noted.

FIGURE 32

Species	Response	Major character	Minor character
Silkworm	Male approach to female	Specific female smell	Other smells Visual characters
water beetle (*Dytiscus*)	prey-catching	Chemical and tactile	Visual
Grayling butterfly (*Eumenis semele*)	Sexual pursuit by male	Dark shade Type of flight Distance	Shape
Domestic hen	Maternal protection of chicks	Distress call	Visual characters
Domestic fowl	Mounting	Crouching posture	Male and female characters

Based on Hinde.
The table shows the important signals which release a particular response in certain animals.

Tinbergen and Perdeck investigated feeding behaviour in the chicks of the herring gull, *Larus argentatus*, and found that it consisted of a chain of activities. The first element is the chick moving towards the parent; a pattern released by the mew call from the parent. After this the pecking response, in which the chick pecks at the beak of the parent, is released by a number of visual stimuli. By using models of the head of an adult herring gull, the investigators could determine the most effective shape and colour. In a series of experiments the parameters (variables) which were important were found to be that the model should be: moving; low; near; have a particular shape with red colouring on the beak, and have an outline of something protruding from the beak. (Figure 33)

A model with a red spot on a yellow beak elicited the greatest response, with black, blue and white spots being progressively less effective, a yellow spot (that is, a completely yellow beak) being least effective of all.

FIGURE 33

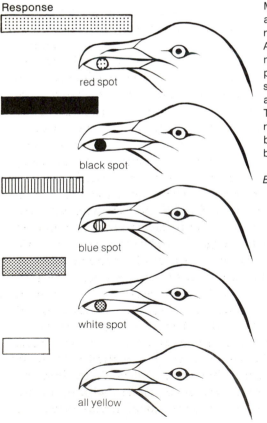

Response

red spot

black spot

blue spot

white spot

all yellow

Model heads used by Tinbergen and Perdeck to elicit the pecking response of young herring gulls. A red spot on a yellow beak was most effective in stimulating the pecking response; other colour spots or no spot at all were less and less effective.

The length of the response bar is related to the number of pecks by the chicks – the longer the bar, the greater the response.

Based on Tinbergen.

Pecking of the adult beak by the chick in turn acts as a releasing stimulus for the parent bird which regurgitates the fish it has just caught. The next element of feeding in the chick, that of swallowing, is released by the tactile stimulus of the fish between the opened bill tips. So this whole feeding pattern has evolved as a reciprocal correlation between releasers in the parents for the chick's behaviour, and releasers in the chick for parental behaviour. Such a correlated pattern, ensures efficiency in the total pattern of feeding the chicks.

Models were also used by Tinbergen in his classic investigation and analysis of the sexual behaviour of the three-spined stickleback, *Gasterosteus*. Here the total reproductive behaviour can be categorised into migratory, territorial, nest building, courtship and parental acts. Increased pituitary, thyroid and gonadal hormones induced by the longer daylength in spring stimulate the male to migrate to warmer, shallower water. Here he selects a territory, motivated by the sight of green vegetation, some of which he uses to build a tunnel shaped nest which is open at each end. Meanwhile his increased gonadal hormones have produced an alteration of his colours and he has developed a bright red belly. It is at this stage that his aggressive territorial behaviour becomes prominent. He guards his territory against intruders which are coloured like himself. By means of models Tinbergen found that it is the redness that matters; a realistic non-red fish provoked little interest, but extremely crude models painted red on their lower surfaces, or even mirrors, all stimulated the stickleback to attack. Border disputes are frequent, in which two competing aggressive males chase each other back and forth over the edges of their adjacent territories. Such disputes do not usually end in injury; very often the two antagonists will suddenly carry out what appears to be completely inappropriate behaviour by standing on their heads and digging in the sandy river bed.

Having acquired his territory, and advertised his ownership, he then waits for a female to swim along. She does not have a red belly and so does not release his aggressiveness; the releasing stimulus presented by her is an abdomen swollen with eggs. Courtship now starts; the male swims towards the female in a zig-zag dance, to which she responds by lifting her head and tail and displaying her swollen abdomen. The male then swims down to the nest, followed by the female. After she has been shown the nest entrance by the male, she enters, her head sticking out of the tunnel at one end and her tail at the other. The male induces her to lay her eggs by prodding her rump with his snout. As soon as she has laid all her eggs she leaves the nest, which is then entered by the male which pours sperm over the eggs. The female is then chased from the nest vicinity and the male repeats the whole pattern with up to five females if available. When the nest contains enough fertilised eggs the male enters his parental, protective stage. He keeps a current of fresh water circulating over the eggs by fanning with his pectoral fins. This activity is proportional to the amount of carbon dioxide in the water around the eggs, and varies inversely with the oxygen concentration. Fanning activity increases during the eight days before the eggs hatch, and then suddenly drops. The male then guards and protects the young, at least as long as his high gonadal hormone level and his red belly colouration last. When he returns to his non-reproductive state he is as likely to eat his own young as any other small fish. Just as in the correlated feeding behaviour of the herring gull chicks and their parents, reproductive behaviour in the stickleback forms a reaction chain. A segment of female behaviour acts as a stimulus for the next stage of male behaviour, which stimulates the next female stage, and so on. The whole system is synchronised in a reproductively efficient way. (Figure 34)

The red colour proved to be the vital aspect of the stickleback model used by Tinbergen, and redness has been shown to be an important signal to other animals. Lack found that a stuffed robin with a normal red breast would be attacked or threatened by other robins. Even a bundle of red feathers, lacking a head, wings, tail, legs or body was attacked, but a complete stuffed adult robin in which the red feathers had been overpainted brown was ignored by birds which had attacked it when in its redbreast condition.

FIGURE 34

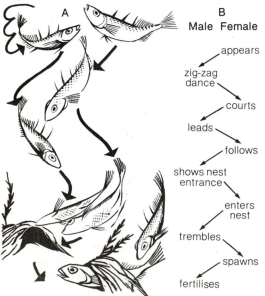

A Shows the sequence of movements (described fully in the text) carried out by male and female sticklebacks.

B Reaction chain in which a segment of behaviour in the male stimulates the next behaviour pattern in the female, and vice versa.

Based on Tinbergen.

B
Male Female

appears

zig-zag
dance

courts

leads

follows

shows nest
entrance

enters
nest

trembles

spawns

fertilises

It is interesting that there is a human association between redness and danger, although it is not known whether this is an innate or an acquired response. It has been known for many years that red, as a background to words and pictures, tends to evoke an emotional reaction, and it is maybe significant that particular regions of the large towns of the world are known as 'red light districts'!

As we have earlier mentioned, the animal must somehow be able to select the 'right' bit of signal information from the background pattern. Such selection could result from filtering mechanisms working at different physiological levels.

The first type, peripheral filtering, depends on the limitations of the sensory equipment. Mechanoreceptors may respond to only a particular frequency of vibration. *Drosophila* males are attracted to a tuning fork producing a specific frequency note, no other frequency giving resonance effects in the sensitive receptor cells. The human visual spectrum is restricted at the lower wavelength end when compared with that of bees which can respond to ultra-violet radiation. (Figure 35)

FIGURE 35

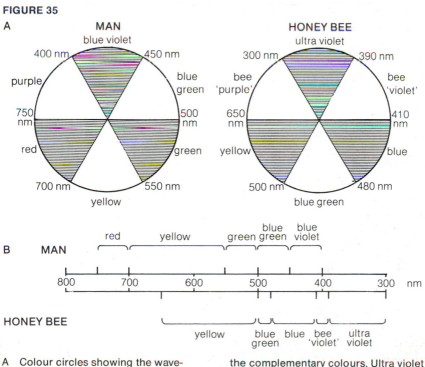

A   Colour circles showing the wavelengths which can be seen by man and the honey bee. The three primary colours are shaded; the opposite segments are the complementary colours. Ultra violet is a primary colour to the honey bee.
B   The visible spectrum to man and the honey bee.

So information of outside events is limited by the properties of the receptor organs. As the experiments using models have shown however, there must also be some filtering of stimuli from the large array to which the receptor organs can respond.

Marler has suggested that there are two other filtering levels involved. One deals with the relationship between the receptor organ and the central nervous system as they work together in normal perception. However it is now becoming evident that a good deal of perceptual filtering goes on within the receptor organ itself, and so the distinction between true peripheral filtering and central stimulus filtering is becoming more blurred.

The other suggested filtering level depends not only on the relationships between the receptor organ and the central nervous system but on the temporal condition of the nervous system. It is known that the response obtained by some releasers depends on the physiological and motivational state of the organism. Drees, in experiments to discover which stimuli evoked courtship behaviour in male jumping spiders which had been reared in isolation, found that the strongest response was given to models with the body divided into two sections, and a pattern of black and white stripes on the abdomen. However outside the breeding season the courtship response disappeared and all models evoked either prey catching or avoidance behaviour, depending on their size. Courtship is not simply evoked by the particular model pattern, but varies according to the hormonal state of the organism. We are now back to our original idea of instinct as a behaviour pattern which depends on an interaction between external factors, the sign stimuli or releasers, and internal factors working within the nervous system of the animal. These internal factors which make up this filtering level perhaps form the equivalent of the innate releaser mechanism postulated by Tinbergen. This he defines as a special neurosensory mechanism which releases the response, and which is susceptible to a special combination of sign stimuli.

The descriptions of the courtship behaviour of the stickleback, or the feeding behaviour of the herring gull chicks, are of instinctive acts carried through under natural conditions to a satisfactory outcome. Releasers have been presented at the right time and in the right sequence, and these, coupled with the necessary internal conditions, have triggered the whole behaviour pattern. In some situations however the internal drive may be so strong as to lead to the completion of the behaviour in the absence of detectable releasing stimuli. A female canary, for example, uses a special weaving movement to push loose strands of material into the cup of its nest, and a bird given neither a nest site nor nesting material will perform the same movement on the floor of its cage. Lorenz described how a well fed starling which had had no opportunity to catch flies for some time went through all the behaviour pattern of catching and killing a non-existent fly. This is vacuum activity, and although it is assumed that it occurs without sign stimuli, it is difficult to prove that there has not been some minute change in the animal's surroundings which triggered the pattern.

Situations also occur, either naturally or experimentally, in which the animal responds more to an excessively stimulating signal than to the normal releaser. Such a supernormal stimulus can evoke a powerful response, and given the choice between the normal and the supernormal stimulus, many animals will choose the supernormal. Baerends found by experiment that herring gulls preferred to incubate artificial eggs which were larger than normal, and would accept and try to sit upon eggs which were so large that brooding became impossible. Eggs which were spottier than normal, or had darker than normal spots were also preferred. The effects of supernormal stimuli can also be seen when different species of birds are kept in the same aviary. The normal reaction of birds to cold air is to raise the feathers and cut heat loss by improving insulation. Such a reflex action makes the bird look larger and more spherical, and when this occurs other birds are stimulated to sit alongside it, the dense group losing less heat than individual birds. If Java sparrows are kept in an aviary with doves, the large size and shape of the dove can present a supernormal feather-raised stimulus to the sparrow, which proceeds to sit against it or even beneath it between the dove's legs. In this case, big is beautiful!

8 The development of behaviour

As we have seen in the last chapter, innate behaviour patterns vary in their rigidity. In some, such as kineses, taxes and some reflexes, there may be a complete and fixed correlation between stimulus and response, at least at a particular age of the animal. However there may be a different response at another age. The ichneumon fly, *Pimpla*, a parasite of the pine shoot moth, *Rhyacionia buoliana*, is repelled by the smell of pine oil early in its adult life, but is attracted as soon as its ovaries ripen. Similarly caterpillars of the large white butterfly, *Pieris brassica*, are gregarious until they reach their last larval stage, when they individually move upwards to pupate on higher walls.

Instinctive acts, depending as they do on external stimuli and internal motivation, are also fixed in their chronological appearance, and are produced at the time in the life cycle at which they are needed. However repetition of instinctive behaviour can lead to modifications which result from experience, and so instinctive acts can become more efficient.

Although most vertebrate behaviour experiments and observations have been carried out with fully formed animals, that is after birth, it is obvious that birth or hatching does not necessarily mean a large neurological change in the animal. A bird which can move around relatively independently as soon as it has hatched, that is a precocial bird, must have the necessary sense organs capable of functioning for some time before hatching. Gottlieb studied the effect of sound on ducklings a day or two before they hatched, and found that they responded with an increased heart rate and that they made more calls themselves. Precocial birds can call before birth when their beaks penetrate into the air space of the egg, enabling them to breathe. This can occur one to three days before hatching. In a natural situation the calls are made in response to auditory signals from the parent birds; a response which has adaptive value. Work by Impekoven on the relationship between parent laughing gulls, *Larus atricilla*, and the chicks within the eggs they were incubating, has shown that the embryo's calls had an effect on the rising and settling pattern of the adult, and also on the rate of egg turning and the amount of parental calling. Vince has demonstrated that embryonic calling has a useful effect on other embryos as well as on the parent birds. He worked with quail embryos which make clicking calls which vary according to the advancement of the embryo. These calls can be heard by all the members of a clutch, and the physiological effect is to accelerate development in 'slow' embryos, and to retard it in 'fast' embryos. This leads to synchronisation of hatching; a useful adaptation for precocial birds which must all be ready to move out of the nest with the mother shortly after hatching.

Such prenatal behaviour is more difficult to show in mammals, although human babies are known to react to sounds for some time before they are born. There is evidence that they are so conditioned to the sound of the mother's heart before they are born that this continues to act as a reassuring signal after birth. Most mothers cradle their infants on their left arm, a position in which the baby is nearer to the mother's heart. This happens in both left handed and right handed mothers, and so is not the result of a right handed mother keeping this arm free to carry out other tasks. Now one recording company has produced a record of a heart beat which it hopes will calm a yelling baby within forty seconds.

Many mammals are precocial and have efficiently working sense organs and locomotion as soon as they are born, and in them complex behaviour patterns can occur very early. Lambs, calves and foals recognise and stay close to their mothers, and are quite capable of moving fast enough to keep up with a herd in the wild. Mammals such as man, other primates, cats and dogs, however, produce altricial offspring which are almost entirely helpless. Their movements are very limited both in kind and degree; their sense organs do not function to the full extent, and their behaviour is stereotyped and restricted. New-born human babies are equipped with a series of reflexes in response to tactile stimuli. A finger touch anywhere on the cheek will evoke the turning of the head towards the finger, the opening of the mouth and grasping movements of the lips, in what is called the 'rooting' reflex. A solid object placed in the baby's palm will produce a very firm grip, and a similar, although not so strong, response occurs as a result of pressure on the sole of the foot. The hand grip response is so strong that the new-born baby can be raised to a sitting position by means of a rod in its hands. This stereotyped behaviour appears to be left over from our evolutionary history. In other primates, particularly in tree dwellers, it is extremely important that the new-born offspring should be able to hold on tightly to the mother, and also be able to find the teat for food. In man these reflexes do not last long, and are replaced by more variable behaviour. The baby learns to focus with its eyes, and can then begin to react to elaborate visual stimulation from the outside world. It is becoming clear that babies can deal with a surprising amount of information at a very early age. They are capable of taking part in a dialogue with their mothers based on sounds and visual signals such as smiling, and can sustain this for an appreciable time even at the age of a few months. As the baby grows older, the vocabulary of signs and sounds used between him and his mother enlarges. Alternative responses now become possible. The baby learns to cope with triangular situations involving his mother, himself and another person. All the time he is being bombarded with stimulation, which he learns to categorise. However what he can deal with at any particular time depends on the state of his nervous system.

Although behaviour patterns can alter as a result of experience, they also change and become more complicated as the nervous system develops and becomes more efficient at dealing with a multiplicity of stimuli. Such development is called maturation. The new-born mammal or bird emerges from a stable environment with limited sensory experience, into surroundings full of new information. The way in which the animal can use this new information depends upon the rate of development of many parts of the body; the sense organs may not work efficiently at first, and muscle systems may be incapable of carrying out needed actions.

One of the earliest investigators into maturation was Spalding who, in 1873, showed that the development of flight in birds was not the result of practice, but rather of the development of the nervous and muscle systems needed to produce the flight movements. He kept young swallows in cages which were too small for them to be able to flap their wings, and compared them with birds which had ample room to make flying movements. Both sets of birds flew when they had reached the right age.

Later Carmichael, in a series of experiments with amphibian tadpoles, reached the conclusion that maturation, and not practice, was important in swimming. He separated a batch of newly hatched salamanders into two groups. Salamanders normally take up to five days making practice swimming movements before they swim well. One group he placed in normal fresh water; the other salamanders were placed in a weak solution of a light anaesthetic. This stopped their movements, but did not affect their growth, as far as he could tell. After the tap water group had reached the behavioural level of swimming, the anaesthetised animals were placed in fresh water. Within thirty minutes they were swimming as well as those which had had five days practice.

So the behaviour of the young animal, whether it is precocial or altricial, depends to a certain extent on the developmental state of the organs needed to carry it out. Given that the young animal has reached the stage of having efficient receptor organs, it becomes obvious that its behaviour will also depend on the amount, and type of stimulation it receives. Many investigators have compared the effects on behaviour of rearing animals in a stimulating or in a restricted environment.

It was found by Rosenzweig and his co-workers that the actual mass of cerebral cortex in rats which had been reared in stimulating surroundings, as in a busy laboratory, or with mazes to learn, or even just boxes to explore, exceeded cortical mass in rats reared in impoverished conditions. Not only had the mass increased; so also had cortical depth and the number of synaptic connections made between neurones.

Laboratory rats which are handled when they are young can cope better in strange circumstances in adult life, and Levine has shown that even momentarily handling infant rats once a day over a period enhances their later ability to be trained to perform simple tasks. A similar improvement of learning capacity in the adult as a result of increased stimulation of the young animal has been shown by Thompson and Melzack to occur in dogs.

Many effects of a lack of stimulation are immediate; animals in a very limited environment, as in the worst zoos, appear bored and carry out abnormal behaviour patterns.

So it appears that a lack of sensory stimulation during early life can have far reaching and permanent effects.

Some classic experiments were carried out in the late 1950s and early 1960s by Harlow on the effects of social deprivation in monkeys. Infant rhesus monkeys, *Macaca mulatta*, were removed from their mothers at an early age, and each was reared in an enclosure which had two surrogate mothers. These were armless models made from rolls of wire netting topped by a not very life like head; one roll of netting was covered with terry towelling, the other was just bare wire. (Figure 36 see next page)

The infants were watched, and the amount of time they spent on each mother was measured. All the infants spent most of their time clinging to the cloth mother, even if it did not supply any milk. The tactile stimulus provided by the terry towelling was important; if milk was only available from bottles suspended within the wire mother, the infants stayed on this model long enough to feed, and then rushed back to the cloth mother. Cloth mothers were accepted even if their heads were made, not only unrealistic, but completely bizarre with large bicycle lamps for eyes. The possibility that cloth mothers were accepted more readily because of their warmth was refuted by the fact that the infants chose to cling to the cloth mother rather than sit on an electrically heated pad on the floor of the cage. In one experiment an infant, reared in a cage with either a cloth or a wire mother, had to pass a

FIGURE.36

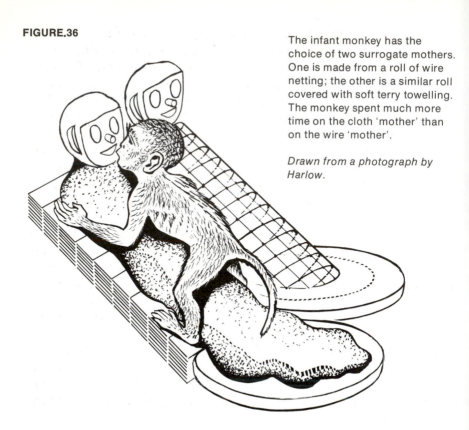

The infant monkey has the choice of two surrogate mothers. One is made from a roll of wire netting; the other is a similar roll covered with soft terry towelling. The monkey spent much more time on the cloth 'mother' than on the wire 'mother'.

Drawn from a photograph by Harlow.

'monster' model in order to reach the surrogate mother. The frightening 'monster' stimuli were varied; sometimes a mechanical jumping grasshopper was used, and sometimes a clockwork teddy bear beating a drum was placed in the cage. All the infants in this situation suffered shock and trauma, but those with a cloth surrogate mother usually managed to get past the 'monster' to jump onto the mother figure. After a time spent clinging to the mother, and apparently getting reassurance by rubbing against the cloth, the infant could usually go to investigate the 'monster' and sometimes destroyed it. Those with wire mothers however did not try to reach them, but crouched near the cage wall, shrieking, sucking their thumbs and appearing to be very distressed.

Harlow analysed the stages of development in normal rhesus monkeys as: reflex, in which the tactile stimulus ensures a gripping response; attachment; security; independence. Infants reared on wire surrogate mothers never really reached the last stage. When they grew up they exhibited various behaviour traits which would be labelled psychotic in man. Sometimes they were hyper-aggressive; sometimes completely withdrawn and non-communicative. Male monkeys grew up sexually incompetent and did not appear to know how to mate; females, if mated, made poor mothers. The degree of abnormality varied with the length of time in which the infants were deprived of contact with all other monkeys. Three months deprivation led to a depressed state from which the monkeys usually recovered; six months gave fairly extensive permanent damage, and one year's isolation gave total personality impairment.

Obviously, then, an environment containing the natural mother and surroundings is essential for the normal psychological development of the rhesus monkey. Does this also apply to other primates, including man? Bowlby in 1951 reported adverse effects of a lack of either a mother, or a reasonably permanent mother figure, on children who were reared in busy institutions, and it was thought that such an 'institutionalised' child was prone to delinquency and long term personality disorders. However further work by Bowlby and his colleagues has suggested that such a result is not necessarily or even commonly found.

What is reasonably clear however is that early experience and stimulation are important in the development of the human personality. From the time it is born, an infant needs a satisfactory relationship either with its mother, or with a mother substitute; a relationship which can be used as a base from which wider group interactions can later develop. Man is a communicating, social animal and it is in the nursery that he first learns this.

In the course of development learning becomes increasingly important, so let us now consider what we mean by learning.

Learning is a change in a behaviour pattern of an animal in response to a given situation as a result of experience, provided that the behaviour change does not result from maturation, or from temporary states of the animal such as fatigue.

Learning can take many different forms; sometimes the learned behaviour pattern is very limited in its scope and soon disappears. Other forms of learning can remain throughout the animal's lifetime.

There are five main classes of learning processes: imprinting; habituation; associative learning; latent learning; insight, and we will consider these more fully in the following chapters.

9 Imprinting and habituation

IMPRINTING

It is obviously important for animals to receive the correct type of stimulation when they are young if they are to develop into successful adults. Birds may respond to parental calls even before hatching and learn to recognise the particular parental sound. In a natural situation many animals hatch or are born into a nest in which the first moving objects they see will be the mother or their nest mates. Spalding, in 1873, was the first investigator to make systematic observations on the responses of very young precocial birds, and he was surprised to find that domestic chicks would follow, not only the mother, but any moving object. Investigations continued with Lorenz in 1937. He divided a clutch of eggs of a grey-lag goose into two batches. One batch he returned to the mother, which incubated and hatched them. The other batch he placed in an incubator, and he himself was the first moving object the goslings saw on hatching. The first group followed the mother about, responding to her calls; the second group had become attached to Lorenz and followed him around. Lorenz called the process 'imprinting' which he described as a type of learning in which the young of precocial birds form an attachment to a 'mother figure'.

Many investigators since then have increased our understanding of imprinting. It is known that many different visual stimuli will induce it. In different experiments moving boxes, bird shaped models, toy balloons, moving and flickering lights, and even the Wellington boots worn by the investigator have resulted in following and apparent attachment by young birds.

Experimental techniques usually involve placing newly hatched birds in an alleyway through which the stimulus object is moved. In an experiment carried out by Sluckin five hundred chicks were individually exposed, one day after hatching, to a small box in a ten foot long alley. Some chicks saw a stationary, and some a moving, box, and the exposure time was also varied. The chicks were then tested at various times after the original exposure by being shown a moving box, and it was found that the strongest following response was shown by those originally exposed to a moving box for the greatest length of time. Hess and Ramsey tested imprinting with mallard ducklings in a circular runway. Mallard eggs were collected regularly and placed in a dark incubator. After they had hatched, the ducklings were kept in individual cardboard boxes so that their visual experience was minimal before they were separately placed in the apparatus. (Figure 37)

Each bird was placed about one foot away from the decoy figure, which was a model of a male mallard, containing a loudspeaker emitting male mallard calls. The decoy was moved slowly round just inside the circular track, and the duckling followed it during a ten minute experimental session. The duckling was then returned to its cardboard box through a trap door in the floor of the runway. The extent of imprinting was tested by subsequently releasing the duckling equidistantly between male and female mallard models, the male emitting the experimental sound, and the female making the normal 'female calling young' sound. All the ducklings followed the male model on which they had been imprinted. In some of these experiments the ducklings had to climb over small barriers placed across the runway, and it was found that the strength of imprinting increased in proportion to the amount of effort involved.

With mallard ducklings imprinting depends on the presentation of auditory as well as visual signals, and this is also important for some other species. Domestic chicks, for example, imprint particularly

FIGURE 37

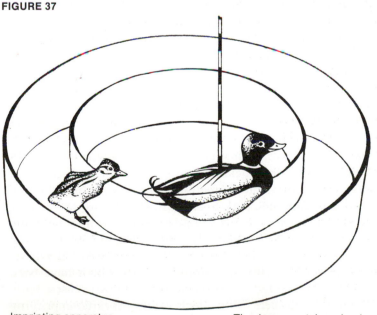

Imprinting apparatus.
The duckling is placed in the circular runway, and the decoy male mallard figure is moved around within the central section.

The decoy contains a loudspeaker which emits a male mallard call.
The duckling follows the decoy figure around the run-way.

Drawn from a photograph by Hess.

strongly on short duration sounds of between about 50 Hz to 400 Hz, and such low pitched short calls retain their attractiveness to the chick. Mallards, if reared in auditory isolation, will approach a variety of low, rhythmic sounds.

In some cases auditory imprinting is of great importance. Wood-ducks, *Aix sponsa*, hatch into restricted nests in holes in hollow trees and, as there is very little light there, cannot visually imprint on the mother. Instead they imprint on the 'kuk-kuk' calls she begins to make just before the eggs hatch, and which increase in intensity as the time for leaving the nest approaches. The mother then flies down to the ground, and again calls the young. One by one the ducklings climb over the rim of the nest hole to tumble down, in some cases as far as sixty feet, to the ground. When the mother hears no more sound from the nest, she moves away followed by her brood.

Through observation and experiments it became obvious that there is a sensitive period in the life of the young bird, although there has been some discussion as to the length of this sensitive period. Some workers, including Hess and Ramsey, found a very short period, as little as between the tenth and twentieth hour of life in mallard ducklings, in which the bird can form a lasting attachment to an object it may see only once. Boyd and Fabricius, however, found that mallard ducklings will follow a moving object on their first exposure to it at any time during their first ten days. These ducklings did not, however, form a lasting attachment to the particular moving object, and so the sensitivity shown is of a different type. Mallard ducklings do not normally leave the nest until the second day, and by then they have passed the peak of the sensitive period for imprinting. This means that even if they haven't all become imprinted upon the mother bird, they might well be imprinted upon each other. So even if only a few of the brood follow the mother, the others will follow them. This very efficient arrangement allows the mother to shepherd all the ducklings to the pond, and explains the orderly family processions which sometimes hold up London traffic as a duck family moves from one park to another. (Figure 38)

Although at first experiments were carried out to find more and more novel objects which would induce imprinting in young birds, it soon became clear that this could have long term and potentially disastrous effects on the experimental animals. Birds which have been experimentally imprinted on cardboard boxes have subsequently attempted to mate with them. The effects of intra-specific imprinting have been found in a number of species of domesticated birds in which individuals of one colour breed have been reared by foster parents of a different colour. Lill and Wood-Gush found that ducks and domestic fowl paired preferentially with the foster parent colour on which they

FIGURE 38

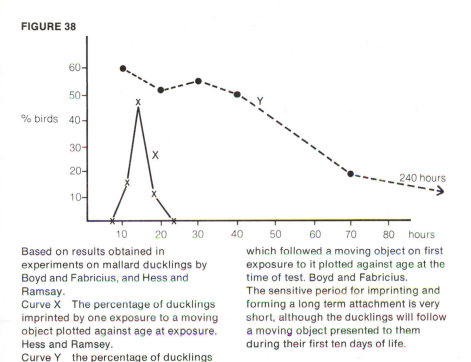

Based on results obtained in experiments on mallard ducklings by Boyd and Fabricius, and Hess and Ramsay.
Curve X   The percentage of ducklings imprinted by one exposure to a moving object plotted against age at exposure. Hess and Ramsey.
Curve Y   the percentage of ducklings which followed a moving object on first exposure to it plotted against age at the time of test. Boyd and Fabricius.
The sensitive period for imprinting and forming a long term attachment is very short, although the ducklings will follow a moving object presented to them during their first ten days of life.

were imprinted. Other effects may be the result of inter-specific imprinting, and experiments have shown that some altricial birds can imprint on their foster parents. Immelmann in 1967 interchanged eggs between clutches of the Zebra finch, *Taeniopygia guttata castanotis*, the Bengalese finch, *Lochura striata f. domestica*, and the African Silver Bill, *Euodice cantans*, allowing the young birds to be reared by the foster parents until the young had reached independence. The young birds were then isolated from the foster parents, and it was found that when the males matured they mated with females of the foster parent species if possible.

Such imprinting can occur between young birds and species as distantly related to them as man. At least twenty-five species of birds which have been hand reared have shown that they can become sexually imprinted on humans and therefore unable to mate with their own species. This is something to consider when one is confronted with the possibility of starting to hand rear a very young bird for whatever reason. In other experiments two closely related species have been used, and this can lead to hybridisation and the development of behaviour patterns which are abnormal for either species. Harris, working on the islands of Skokholm and Skomer off the Welsh coast, found that it was possible to produce hybrids between *Larus argentatus*, the herring gull, and *Larus fuscus*, the lesser black backed gull. The British herring gull rarely moves more than 240 kilometres from its hatching site, but most lesser black backed gulls overwinter in Spain, Portugal or on the North West coast of Africa. In a series of experiments in 1962 and 1963 Harris interchanged eggs between herring gull and lesser black backed gull nests, and then ringed the emerging young birds. 407 herring gull chicks were reared by lesser black backed gull foster parents, and 335 lesser black backed gull chicks were reared by herring gull foster parents. When the chicks had grown enough to migrate, herring gulls turned up in the wintering areas of the lesser black backed gulls. When Harris returned to Skokholm in 1968, he found 29 mixed pairs of gulls, all of which were in the small colonies where he had interchanged the eggs. The results suggest that the young birds had imprinted upon their foster parents and thereafter behaved like them.

Although most of the experimental work on imprinting has been carried out on birds, it has long been known that in order to train mammals one must start when they are very young. Dogs become tame if they have early experience of people, and it is this exposure, rather than any rewards, which produces docility as the dog matures. Orphaned lambs can imprint upon their human rearers, and most zoo animals which have been hand reared by keepers turn out to be useless for breeding later on.

As we have seen in the previous chapter, it is essential for human babies to have a mother figure to whom they can relate during their early lives. To begin with social responses are elicited by a wide range of stimuli, but gradually these are reduced to those arising from one, or a small number of individuals. The strength of the attachment made depends on the time spent with the mother figure, and in most infants this strong attachment is made during the time between six weeks and nine months of age. After this time, the baby is more likely to respond to strangers with fear responses, and so the development of an attachment to a new figure becomes more difficult towards the end of the first year.

This development of human attachment behaviour does not meet the criteria originally laid down by Lorenz for imprinting – (i) that it takes place *only* during a brief critical period in the life cycle; (ii) that it is irreversible; (iii) that it influences patterns of behaviour that have not yet developed in the organism's repertoire such as sexual behaviour; and (iv) that it is behaviour which occurs in a young, precocial bird in learning to follow a moving object.

The concept of imprinting, however, has altered since Lorenz first described it. It is no longer seen to be a unique learning process which occurs rapidly and without apparent reward in precocial birds only, and the way in which attachment behaviour in the human infant becomes focussed on a discriminated person is sufficiently similar to imprinting in birds as to be included in a much wider use of the term. Such an attachment to a specific mother figure gives the baby more protection from danger, and also provides a situation in which the young child can learn by imitating the mother.

HABITUATION

Most people can remember from their childhood one of Aesop's fables about the shepherd boy who cried 'Wolf'.

To refresh your memory: the story concerns a shepherd boy who, becoming bored and lonely while minding his flock all day, decided to cause some excitement and possibly get some company by rushing to the villagers crying 'Wolf, wolf'. Immediately all the villagers rushed out to help him protect his flock. He was so delighted with the results of his action that he repeated it a few days later, and again the villagers rushed out. However when he cried 'Wolf, wolf' the third time, there was no response from the villagers. They had learned to ignore the signal. Unfortunately this time there really was a wolf which carried off the best sheep from the flock. As the story is a fable, there must be a moral in it somewhere, and so the wise man of the village said 'A liar will not be believed, even when he speaks the truth'.

As animal behaviourists we are not concerned with the morality of the shepherd boy, but the behaviour of the villagers makes a good starting point for our next topic.

If an animal is repeatedly stimulated, without either reward or punishment, then it will cease to respond. Birds are, at first, fearful of a scarecrow, but continued exposure to such a static, harmless object eventually produces no response at all. The birds may simply ignore it, or may use it as a perch, or even as a source of nesting material. This loss of the original response is called 'habituation', and it involves learning to ignore stimuli which are found not to be a threat. Unlike other forms of learning, habituation is not the acquisition of new responses but the loss of old ones. It is possible that, as the information about the stimulus has to be received by sense organs, the loss of response is due to sensory adaptation. This has been shown not to be the case in the habituation shown by certain fan worms to tactile stimulation of the tentacles. At first the worm withdraws into its tube, but after repeated stimulation it fails to respond in this way. Obviously the sensory cells in the tentacle could have adapted and become incapable of initiating an action potential. However, if this were the case, then stimulation of other sensory cells within the same tentacle should restart the response. That this does not occur means that the block occurs, not at the receptor level, but within the central nervous system of the animal.

Such a central block has been investigated fully in the earthworm. Continued prodding of the head of the worm will gradually reduce the initial, violent withdrawal response produced by longitudinal muscle contraction to very little, and finally no reaction at all. The touch receptors are known to be slow adapting, and the effector organs, the longitudinal muscle fibres, are also known to be capable of working over a very long period without loss of power. So the block must occur somewhere in the central nervous system between the receptors and the effectors. It is known that the median giant fibre is involved in the transmission of impulses from the head end of the worm, and careful experiments by Roberts have shown that the block occurs at the synapses between the afferent and efferent nerve fibres and this median giant fibre.

Habituation is important in adjusting an animal's response to the environment. Clark carried out many investigations into the behaviour of *Nereis pelagica*, a polychaete worm which is common in brackish estuaries. *Nereis* can survive both in fresh water and in fully marine conditions, and so is adapted to estuaries with their alternating fresh water and tidal sea water. The worm lives in burrows in the sandy mud, and protrudes its head and anterior segments to feed on detritus, diatoms, flatworms and various crustaceans. Clark found that the worms could be induced to live in glass tubes in an aquarium, rather than their estuarine mud tubes, and so he could observe their reactions to various stimuli. Many different stimuli evoked a withdrawal response; jarring the aquarium, touching the head, or a sudden shadow on the head end all resulted in the withdrawal of the protruding head into the glass tube, but the worms re-emerged within one minute. If a particular stimulus was repeated at one minute intervals, there was a rapid decline in the percentage of worms responding. Habituation occurred more rapidly if the time gaps between repeated stimuli were small. In one experimental series the worms took 40 flashes at half minute intervals of a bright light to habituate fully, but 80 flashes were needed if there were five minute intervals between consecutive flashes. Different stimuli also produced different habituation times; mechanical shock is much slower than changes in light intensity in inducing habituation. (Figure 39)

A fundamental withdrawal response is advantageous to *Nereis*. Mechanical jarring might be caused by wading birds looking for food, and sudden shadows could result from predatory fish swimming over it. However *Nereis* cannot spend its life withdrawn into a burrow; it must emerge to feed. Passing shadows are much more likely to be floating seaweed than predatory fish, and so it can afford to habituate quickly to sudden changes in light intensity.

Habituation is widespread in animals. Lorenz and Tinbergen, in their investigations into releasers in young ducks and geese, found that fear reactions could be evoked by the movement of a model bird over the pen. (Figure 40)

They found that the young birds showed fear if the model was moved from left to right, thereby appearing to be hawk shaped, but gave no response if the model was moved from right to left, and thus appeared to be duck or goose shaped. This experiment was the starting point for

FIGURE 39

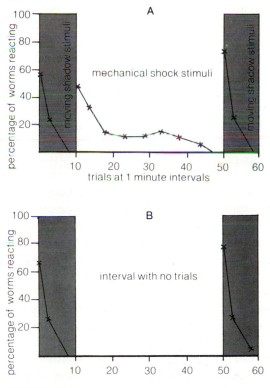

To show habituation to two different stimuli in *Nereis*.
A   The graph shows the percentage of worms which reacted by head withdrawal in trials at one minute intervals. All the worms ceased to respond to a repeated moving shadow stimulus within the first ten trials. If a mechanical shock stimulus, such as jarring the aquarium, was then substituted for the moving shadow, the withdrawal response reappeared in half the worms. Habituation to mechanical shock took much longer, over thirty trials being needed. Moving shadow stimuli again produced a response, showing that habituation is independent for the two types of stimuli.
B   Forty minutes is a sufficient time for the response to moving shadows to reappear in the absence of stimulation.

Based on Clark.

FIGURE 40

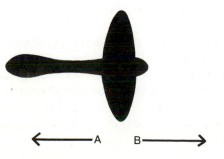

Model bird used by Tinbergen and Lorenz in their investigation into releasers.
If moved in the direction marked B the model looked hawk-like, and elicited fear reactions in the young birds. If moved from right to left, that is in the direction of A, the model was goose shaped, and was ignored by the young birds.

many other investigations. Hirsch found that white leghorn chicks showed no more alarm for movement in one direction than in the other; at first all the chicks were alarmed, but they all quickly habituated and stopped showing fear. Melzack and his co-workers reared mallard ducklings in four groups. In one group the ducklings were given 120 exposures to the hawk shaped model each day from the age of 4 to 21 days, and a second group were exposed in a similar way to the goose shaped model. The other two groups acted as controls and these birds were exposed to neither model. During the experiment, both orienting responses, in which the ducklings looked at, and possibly followed the direction of movement of the model with head movements, and also fear responses, in which the ducklings crouched, and made fright calls, were recorded. When all four groups were exposed, on day 25, to either model, the controls reacted by showing either orienting or fear responses. The experimental animals, however, showed only orienting responses, the fear responses having disappeared. Fear responses also gradually disappeared from the control birds. Even if the hawk shaped model appeared to be harmful to the ducklings on their first exposure to it, they fairly quickly habituated to it. Schneirla criticised the Lorenz and Tinbergen experiment on the grounds that the birds used were not naive and could have learned the difference between hawks and geese, and that they scored group and not individual responses. He suggested that the hawk model was alarming because its broad leading edge would result in a more abrupt darkening of the bird's visual field, and predicted that the same result could be obtained by a triangle moved base forwards – a prediction which was not upheld by experiment. With turkey chicks the alarm response can be elicited with a model of any shape provided that it is moved at the correct speed of between five and ten model lengths per second, a speed which corresponds well to the apparent speed of birds of prey in flight. However the turkeys rapidly cease to respond to familiar models.

Habituation is a useful way of preventing the complete restriction of behaviour in response to stimulation. It is important that young birds can react to potentially dangerous situations, but also that they can habituate to such stimuli as moving leaves or other harmless objects. It is also important that the original response is not completely obliterated, but can spontaneously recover over a period without stimulation.

Habituation is the temporary loss of a response, as a result of continued stimulation, in situations where the response is not needed. Most other kinds of learning are concerned with the strengthening, not the loss, of adaptive responses.

10 Associative learning and latent learning

ASSOCIATIVE LEARNING

In associative learning the animal learns to associate a particular behaviour pattern with reward or punishment.

Psychologists distinguish between two types of associative learning according to the experimental situations involved in the learning process. One type is now called Pavlovian or classical conditioning, as the technique was developed by the distinguished Nobel Laureate, Ivan Pavlov in the early years of the twentieth century. The other experimental situation was developed by Professor B. F. Skinner of Harvard University, based on earlier work by Thorndike, and is known as operant or instrumental conditioning.

PAVLOVIAN CONDITIONING

Most people have some knowledge of Pavlov's dogs, and the production of conditioned reflexes. A dog will normally salivate at the sight, smell or taste of food. Pavlov presented the natural stimulus of food to a dog, but also gave an indifferent or neutral stimulus, such as a bell. After the combined stimuli had been presented many times, the neutral stimulus alone was enough to produce salivation. So the basic, useful reflex action 'taste of meat ⟶ salivation' had been replaced by 'bell ⟶ salivation'. Pavlov called the process conditioning, and the new behaviour a conditioned reflex.

This brief description suggests that the experimentation was extremely easy. In fact the experiments required the use of very careful controls. If the dog was to be presented with two types of stimulation simultaneously, then all background stimulation had to be carefully standardised as it could not be completely eliminated. This meant that the investigator could not be present in the room and so there had to be some automatic device for delivering food to the dog. A standard amount of meat powder was therefore puffed through a tube into the dog's mouth. The presence of this tube meant that the dog had to be immobilised in a harness, and this permitted the presence of a tube passing from a salivary duct, through the dog's cheek, to a measuring flask. (Figure 41 see next page)

Many different experiments were carried out using varied combinations and timing of stimuli. In one series Pavlov preceded each ration of meat powder by setting a metronome ticking. To begin with there was no response, but after five or six trials the dog began to salivate before the meat powder arrived in its mouth. It had learned to associate the sound of the metronome with the forthcoming meat powder and to respond accordingly. Before conditioning, the meat powder or unconditioned stimulus evoked salivation, the unconditioned response. After conditioning, the metronome or conditioned stimulus, evoked salivation, which had now become the conditioned response. In this example the response results from the association of the new stimulus with a reward, the meat powder, and this is called positive reinforcement.

The animal may also acquire conditioned reflexes as a result of an unpleasant original, unconditioned stimulus from which it wishes to escape. If a dog is given an electric shock in its foot (an unconditioned stimulus), its normal reflex action is to withdraw its leg (the unconditioned response). If a bell (the conditioned stimulus) is rung at the same time as the shock is given then the dog will learn to withdraw its leg for the bell alone (the conditioned response). This is called negative reinforcement.

FIGURE 41

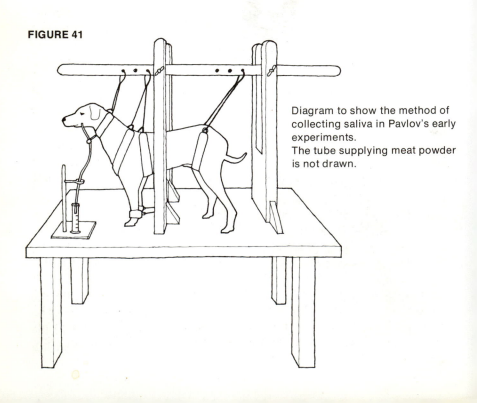

Diagram to show the method of collecting saliva in Pavlov's early experiments.
The tube supplying meat powder is not drawn.

In both of these examples reinforcement occurs with the presentation of the unconditioned stimulus – a reward with the meat powder and punishment with the electric shock – and so this type of conditioning is sometimes called Type S conditioning (S for stimulus).

The conditioned stimulus used in such experiments may be precise, or it may be part of a class of stimuli. A dog, for example, which has been conditioned to salivate to a tone of 1000 Hz, is also likely to salivate to one of 900 Hz but the amount of salivation will be less. This is known as stimulus generalisation and it can prevent the animal from learning to respond to a precise stimulus. However if the dog which salivates to a wide range of tones is subjected to a series of trials in which the specific, wanted tone is always followed by the meat powder, and in which the other tones never are, then it will quickly learn to discriminate between them.

By such experimental methods, one of Pavlov's dogs was conditioned to discriminate between a circle and an ellipse. The ellipse was then gradually changed so that it looked more and more like a circle and, as expected, the dog lost its discriminatory ability and salivated to the wrong stimulus. The loss of discrimination was accompanied by other behaviour changes; a previously docile dog became irritable and snappy, and Pavlov described it as exhibiting 'neurotic symptoms'.

Pavlov also found that he could produce what he called 'higher-order' conditioning. To begin with, he trained a dog to associate the sound of a metronome with meat powder in the usual way. When the dog salivated for the sound of the metronome presented alone, he showed it a black square with the metronome. The metronome had already acquired the capacity to evoke salivation, and so could be used as a positive reinforcer in place of the meat powder. After a series of presentations of the metronome and the black square, the dog began to salivate for the black square alone. This second-order conditioned response was considerably weaker than the first order conditioned response, and Pavlov found it impossible to establish a third-order conditioned response.

The development of conditioned reflexes does not only occur inside a laboratory. The black and yellow banded caterpillars of the cinnabar moth, *Hipocrita jacobaeae*, have a cuticle which is distasteful to birds, which soon learn to associate the bad taste with the black and yellow pattern. Any other insect, whether distasteful or not, which has the same type of black and yellow warning colouration will then be avoided by birds. Obviously a palatable, easily preyed upon, insect will gain an advantage if it can mimic such a distasteful model and so avoid being eaten. Such mimicry was first observed by H. W. Bates in 1862 and is now called Batesian mimicry.

It is also advantageous for distasteful animals to mimic each other. As it takes a certain number of trials before a predator will have been conditioned to associate a particular pattern with a bad taste, each particular animal will benefit as these trials are shared between them. This adoption of a particular warning colouration by distasteful, and often poisonous, animals, which is known as Mullerian mimicry, is widespread. The black and yellow striped pattern, for instance, is seen not only on wasps and bees, but also on some poisonous snakes and other reptiles, and seems to be a commonly recognised and avoided pattern.

A further naturally acquired conditioned reflex is seen in bullfrogs, *Rana catesbeiana*, which can quickly learn where food is available in their natural surroundings. Frogs are 'passive' hunters and wait for insects to move within striking distance, so it is important that the frogs can place themselves in the best positions for this. Van Bergeijk noticed that a colony of bullfrogs in his laboratory could anticipate feeding time by gathering round the feeding trough several hours in advance of their normal feeding session. A series of experiments showed that this anticipatory behaviour was not just the working of an internal clock in the frog which made it look for food at a fixed time each day. By changing the time and place of feeding, the investigators showed that the frogs had to relearn their pattern but also that they could do so surprisingly quickly. The actual nature of the conditioning stimulus was the start of general activity in the laboratory on a working day; on holidays there was no anticipatory behaviour. The frogs then responded a certain time later by aggregating at the feeding trough. They could lose a particular response, and acquire a new one rapidly if the time and place of feeding were altered. Frogs and toads are not easy to train by the usual laboratory methods, but this series of experiments suggests that they are fast learners for certain behaviour patterns.

OPERANT CONDITIONING

In Pavlovian conditioning the reinforcement, whether positive as in the meat powder or negative as in the electric shock, evokes the response. The new conditioning stimulus given with the original stimulus will also eventually evoke the response. With either the unconditioned or the conditioned stimulus, the stimulus must come first and the response follows and it is the stimulus which acts as the reinforcer.

Another way of experimentally dealing with the reinforcement is to associate it, not with the stimulus, but with the response. This is known as Type R conditioning (R for response) and it is also sometimes called 'instrumental' conditioning as the response is instrumental in producing the reinforcer. Most of the experimental evidence comes from the behaviour of small laboratory animals such as rats, mice or pigeons in a special box, devised by Skinner, now called a Skinner box. Skinner boxes vary in detail, but each has a lever or a bar which operates a food supply mechanism. A rat placed in a Skinner box will sniff around, particularly into the corners, and is likely to press the lever by chance. Immediately the rat receives a food pellet down a chute. The rat has therefore altered its environment by means of its own behaviour. The muscle movement of pressing the lever, that is the response, occurs before the food, that is the reinforcer, appears. We can say that the reinforcer is contingent upon the response, and we call the behaviour of pressing the lever the operant. The pressing of the lever is originally accidental; the rat has no experience of the mechanism of the box, and there is no reason for any part of the box to be particularly important to the rat. However as soon as the food appears, the particular behaviour happening at the time becomes associated with it. We can say that the food is a reward to the rat, but it is more useful to see it as something which reinforces a particular bit of behaviour. The next time the rat is placed in the Skinner box it is slightly more likely to press the lever, and the food reinforcement makes it even more likely the third time. So the animal learns to press the lever as soon as it is placed in the box. Obviously in order to train a rat by means of food reinforcement it is necessary to start the process with a hungry animal.

In this basic experiment the rat is making a normal movement and this segment of behaviour is automatically reinforced. It is however possible to train an animal into a behaviour pattern which is not in its normal repertoire. Imagine that the investigator wants to train an animal to press a coloured disc high on the side wall of a Skinner box. Each time the animal turns towards the disc, during random movements, the operator works the food mechanism. That bit of behaviour will therefore be reinforced, and the animal gradually learns to press the required disc. It is like a slow version of the children's party game in which a child who has been sent out of the room has to come in and find an object chosen by the rest, the only clues being praise if she moves in the right direction (positive reinforcement) and scolding if she goes the wrong way (negative reinforcement). Each time the experimental animal moves nearer to the required object it is given food. Such a process of encouraging bits of approximately correct behaviour is called 'shaping'. Skinner trained a rat to pull a string to release a marble from a rack, to pick the marble up in its paws, to carry it to another part of the cage, and finally to lift it up and drop it down a tube two inches from the floor of the cage. Each step was carried out by reinforcing approximations, and this is the basic way of training animals to carry out the un-natural behaviour patterns seen in circuses.

This association of the reinforcement with the behaviour immediately preceding it can have unexpected results. If an experimental animal is doing something else at the same time as it presses the lever in a Skinner box, then both the lever pressing and the something else will be reinforced. The animal then learns the total pattern, one movement of which is useful, and the other movement which has no particular value. A monkey, for example, might well be scratching its head when it presses the lever, and it quickly learns to do this whenever it subsequently presses the lever. Skinner refers to the head scratching as 'superstitious' behaviour; it has nothing to do with the causal relationship of the lever and the food mechanism. In one experiment a hungry pigeon was placed in a Skinner box in which it had learned to feed from a grain hopper. (Figure 42) The food supply was then operated periodically, small quantities of grain appearing at 30 second intervals throughout several long experimental sessions. The appearance of the food was not now contingent on a particular behaviour pattern. However the pigeon was doing something at the time the food appeared, and this behaviour was reinforced. This gave a slightly increased chance that the pigeon would be doing the same thing when the next lot of grain appeared, and so the behaviour pattern became stronger. The pigeon gets trapped into a particular behaviour sequence which may appear to be completely bizarre. In some experiments Skinner found that the pigeons developed behaviour patterns which included turning sharply to one side, hopping from one foot to the other, bowing and finally lifting the head high.

FIGURE 42

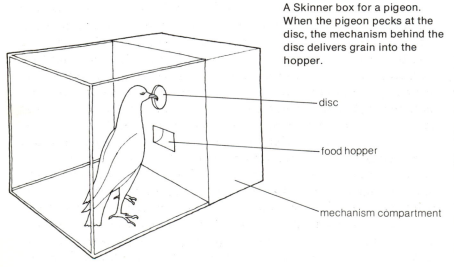

A Skinner box for a pigeon. When the pigeon pecks at the disc, the mechanism behind the disc delivers grain into the hopper.

disc

food hopper

mechanism compartment

Such a situation may seem amusing. With our greater wisdom we can laugh at the monkey 'knowing' that it must scratch its head in order to obtain food. We know that there is no causal connection between these two actions. We must not be too condescending however; think of the frequency with which people behave in a similar way. A particular article of clothing worn during a day on which all goes well becomes lucky. Large numbers of people are convinced that their lives will run smoothly as long as they have their mascots with them. A widespread form of superstitious reinforcement occurs during illness. Many diseases run through a natural development, and a remedy given at the time when the patient is on the point of recovering naturally is reinforced by this recovery. So we have inherited some very strange folk remedies and beliefs, all of which have been 'proven' to work.

The behaviour of animals in a Skinner box is one way of demonstrating operant conditioning. A rather more flexible apparatus is a maze, which can range in difficulty from a simple T or Y junction, to a long series of junctions to be negotiated by the animal. Mazes are particularly useful because of this variability; earthworms or flatworms can be conditioned in the simplest type, while rats are capable of learning the way through mazes with many junctions. The 'correct' behaviour may be positively reinforced by food at the end of the maze, or the animal may be given an electric shock if it takes a wrong turning, and this behaviour is negatively reinforced.

Many different species of animals have been investigated for maze learning ability. The lower invertebrates such as earthworms and planarians can learn only the simplest maze, and do not retain the learning for very long. Insects are much better. Bees can learn their way to food in a maze centre, but are not very good at finding their way out again. Weiss found that they could quickly be trained to turn left when faced by a blue screen and right at a yellow screen, at least if these screens were before the bees reached the food. After they had eaten they were confused by either a blue or a yellow screen, and had to learn the answer to the problem all over again. (Figure 43 page 88) Ants are particularly good at learning the way through complicated mazes, but there are individual differences, some ants coping better than others.

No matter which animal is being investigated, its performance, measured by the number of mistakes and the time taken, improves with the number of trials it has in the maze. (Figure 44) As there is a minimum time needed for the actual movement through the maze, once this point is reached no further improvement in the time taken is possible.

A third experimental technique of operant conditioning has been used particularly with octopuses. An octopus is kept in an aquarium tank where it lurks between rocks. If a moving crab is lowered into the

FIGURE 43

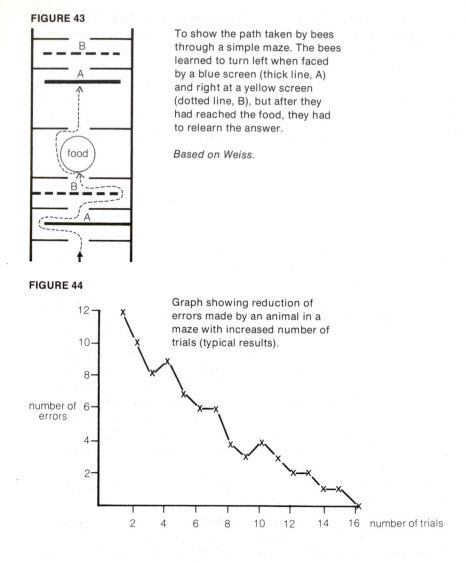

To show the path taken by bees through a simple maze. The bees learned to turn left when faced by a blue screen (thick line, A) and right at a yellow screen (dotted line, B), but after they had reached the food, they had to relearn the answer.

Based on Weiss.

FIGURE 44

Graph showing reduction of errors made by an animal in a maze with increased number of trials (typical results).

other end of the tank, the octopus will quickly move out and attack it. If, however, the investigator lowers a white square into the tank at the same time as he lowers the crab, the octopus is given an electric shock when it attacks the crab. The training schedule consists of three trials of the crab and white square, and therefore electric shock, and three trials of the crab alone, and no electric shock, each day over a period of time. The octopus soon learns to associate the white square with an unpleasant sensation, and no longer attacks the crab displayed with the white square. Crabs displayed alone continue to be attacked.

'Trial and error' experiments can take many forms as we have seen, but they all contain the situation that the animal is rewarded in some way if it carries out the experimentally 'correct' action, and is punished if it makes a mistake. Animals vary in the time taken to learn to perform the task without error, and also in how complex a task they can learn. Some learn better through positive, some through negative reinforcement. The principles involved in operant conditioning have been applied by Professor Skinner to human learning, and he was the inventor of one of the first 'teaching machines'. We shall return to this topic in a later chapter.

The two types of conditioning, Pavlovian and operant, have certain characteristics in common.

Contiguity

If either a conditioned stimulus in Pavlovian conditioning, or a new response in operant conditioning is to be associated with a reinforcement, then the reinforcement must be close to it in time.

There are stringent time relationships in the build up of a conditioned reflex. If the unconditioned stimulus precedes the conditioned stimulus there is very little conditioning. The reversed situation of the conditioned stimulus preceding the unconditioned stimulus will be effective, as long as there is neither a time gap between the end of the conditioned stimulus and the beginning of the unconditioned stimulus, nor a continuation of the conditioned stimulus after the unconditioned stimulus has stopped. This means that, with our example of the dog, the metronome and the meat powder, it is no good giving the meat powder before the metronome, or letting the metronome run on after the meat powder has stopped. What is needed is the metronome first, and then the meat powder.

In operant conditioning the reinforcer, the food pellet, must appear shortly after the response, or learning is very slow. In animal training when it may be difficult to present a reward quickly enough, it is usually possible to overcome the problem by introducing a secondary reinforcement. A rat in a Skinner box may learn that it will receive a food pellet after a light has been switched on by its lever pressing; the rat will then press the lever to light the lamp. This forms a bridging stimulus between the response and the primary reinforcement of food.

Repetition

Most associative learning improves on repetition. As we have seen, the time an animal takes to run through a maze decreases with the number of trials, and an animal in a Skinner box requires a certain amount of practice in order to go straight to the lever. In Pavlovian conditioning long repetition of the simultaneous presentation of the conditioned and the unconditioned stimuli strengthens the response.

Physiological State

The speed of each type of conditioning depends on the physiological state of the experimental animal. Reinforcement of the behaviour pattern with food does not work with a well fed animal, and so the type of reinforcement must be suitable for the experimental circumstances. However if an animal is extremely hungry, this also interferes with the learning process; it is as if the animal cannot concentrate on anything but its hunger. Some interesting experiments by Olds and Milner showed that electrical stimulation of some areas of the brain of rats was rewarding in itself. Rats with electrodes implanted in part of the hypothalamus were placed in a Skinner box, which had been altered so that pressing the lever passed a very small current through the electrodes. The rats behaved as though this gave them pleasure, and continued to press the lever at phenomenal rates; in one case at over 7000 presses per hour until exhaustion overtook the animal. Such a 'pleasure centre' is presumably the area of the brain which would be stimulated by the normal reward, and certainly electrodes implanted in the part of the hypothalamus which controls eating will cause the animal to behave in the same way as if it is rewarded with food.

Extinction

If, when an animal has developed a conditioned reflex, the conditioned stimulus is continually given without periodic reinforcement with the unconditioned stimulus, then the conditioned reflex will disappear in a process called extinction. Thinking again of our example of the dog, the metronome and the meat powder; the continued presentation of the metronome alone once the conditioned reflex has been built up will result in the loss of the reflex. (Figure 45)

A conditioned reflex will spontaneously recover after extinction if the conditioned stimulus is given again, although it does not reach its earlier strength and subsequent extinction occurs more rapidly. Pavlov

FIGURE 45

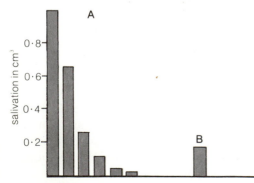

Results obtained by Pavlov, 1925, on experimental extinction of a conditioned salivation reflex.
A Amount of salivation in trials at 3 minute intervals without the unconditioned stimulus.
B Spontaneous recovery shown in a single trial after a 20 minute gap.

regarded extinction not as the loss of a learned process, but as the result of new learning which inhibited the conditioned reflex. Extinction is useful in natural conditions; it is physiologically wasteful for an animal to go on making a response when there is no further chance of reinforcement.

It is much more difficult to extinguish an operant response. In a Skinner box the lever pressing activity will continue even if only 1 in 100 presses results in food arriving to reinforce the behaviour. An analogy with the behaviour of people playing one-armed bandit gambling machines is not hard to see.

LATENT OR EXPLORATORY LEARNING

One of the vital concepts of associative learning is the importance of the reinforcer. As we have seen, it is not only its presence which is needed; it must be presented at the right time for learning to occur.

With this in mind, consider some maze experiments carried out by Tolman and Honzik in which they trained rats in a maze in which there were fourteen T junctions at which the rats could turn left or right. Rats in one group were subjected to normal maze training, reinforced by food, and their performance, judged by a decreasing number of errors, steadily improved. By the 11th day they had learned the maze fairly well. Other rats were placed in a similar maze, but this time no food was given. There was therefore no motivation to learn one path rather than another. This procedure was followed with a third group of rats. With no food in the maze, their performances were similar to those in group two. However food was placed at the end of the maze on day 11, and these rats could suddenly run the maze; their errors dropped as low as those of group one by day 12. (Figure 46)

FIGURE 46

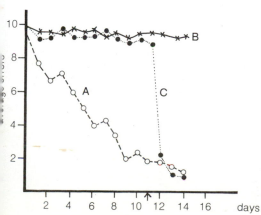

Based on experimental results of Tolman and Honzik, 1930, with rats in a 14 unit maze of multiple T type.
A   Rats regularly rewarded with food.
B   Rats not given food in maze.
C   Rats not rewarded with food until day 11.

Had the rats learned the pattern of the maze while they were carrying out exploratory behaviour, and while there was no reinforcement? It certainly appeared that this was the case. Many animals learn their local geography in great detail by just such exploratory behaviour. In these experiments food was regarded as being the only reinforcer. However it has been shown by Montgomery that rats will learn their way through a maze for the reward of having a new area to explore at the end. Novelty is important to many animals. A new situation is carefully explored even if there does not appear to be any rewarding stimulus. We must not jump to conclusions about rewards; they may well be present for the experimental animal even if we cannot immediately see what they are. Thorpe has defined latent learning as 'the association of indifferent stimuli or situations without patent reward'.

11 Insight learning and reasoning

Most workers have used the term 'insight' when they have seen animals solving problems without using trial and error behaviour. Very often, when in a problematic situation, the animal will sit, apparently doing nothing, until suddenly it gets up and carries out a behaviour pattern which solves the problem. This suggests that, during the time when the animal appears to be doing nothing it is making mental 'trial and error' deductions. This is, of course, what we do ourselves. We do not need actually to carry out trials; we can reason things out, considering various possible courses of action and then choose the behaviour most likely to solve the problem. To do this we depend upon our previous experience and use the knowledge we have gained in the context of the new problem. Maier defines reasoning as 'the ability to combine spontaneously two or more separate or isolated experiences to form a new experience which is effective for obtaining the desired end'.

The first systematic experiments on insight learning were carried out by Kohler with a colony of chimpanzees on Tenerife, between 1913 and 1917. Kohler was a *Gestalt* psychologist who was interested in the reactions of animals to the complete visual pattern of stimulation, and the inter-relationships between the relevant parts of the problem.

He devised two main types of problems in which the chimpanzee could see, but could not at first reach, some bananas. In the first set of experiments a chimpanzee was put into a cage which had a banana hanging from the roof. A box was also placed in the cage and, by placing this beneath the hanging banana and jumping up from it, the chimpanzee could reach the fruit. This proved a difficult problem for most of the chimpanzees, and only one out of seven, an ape named Sultan, solved it without help. Some of the others managed to get the banana if the box was left in the correct place for them. Although the solution seems easy to us, it requires an appreciation of the necessary spatial relationship between the box and the banana, and a realisation that jumping is also needed. When the apes had found the solution they would walk away from the banana to fetch the box. This reversal of the simple food approach behaviour suggested that the apes saw the box and banana, not as unconnected isolated objects, but as related parts of a problem solving whole pattern. The chimpanzees were then tested in a similar, but taller, cage but this time they were given two boxes. In order to reach the hanging banana the chimpanzee had to stand one box on top of the other and then climb upon them. This required insight into using two boxes to double the height gained, but also required skill in making the two boxes stable. (Figure 47)

In the second experimental series the banana was outside the cage and the chimpanzee was given one or more sticks. To begin with, the chimpanzees threw their sticks at the bananas, and so lost them. However they soon learned to use a stick as an extension of the arm, and could draw the banana into the cage. Sultan, the chimpanzee which did best in the whole series of experiments, coped very well with a variation of this problem. He was given a length of soft straw instead of a stick; although the straw was long enough to reach the banana, it was not rigid enough to be able to draw the fruit towards the cage. Sultan bent the straw, which increased its rigidity, and then bent it again. The fact that the bundle of straw was now too short to reach the banana does not detract too much from an inventive solution. In another experiment Sultan was given two sticks, each of which was too short to reach the banana. He couldn't solve the problem until he had, by chance, one stick in each hand and they were in a straight line. He then immediately fitted one stick into the end of the other, thereby doubling the available length, and drew in the banana, and everything else he could reach.

Kohler's explanation and interpretation of these experiments claimed that the apes showed intelligence in solving the problems. As the apes mentally 'saw' the solution he called them 'insight' experiments. Further insight experiments with chimpanzees were carried out in the 1920s by Yerkes, who drew up certain criteria for insight learning.

FIGURE 47
The chimpanzee needed to place one box on another directly beneath the banana in order to reach it – an insightful solution.

FIGURE 48
The 'detour' problem.
The dog can reach the food only if it first walks away from it and round the post.

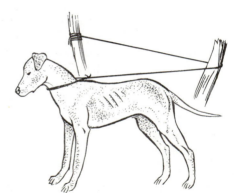

Since then many experimental techniques have been used. One of the simplest is the 'detour' problem. (Figure 48)

A dog is tied to a post by a lead which is long enough for the dog to reach a bowl of food as long as the lead is not caught round another post. In this situation the dog must turn its back on the food, walk back round the second post, and then it will be able to reach the dish. Dogs find this to be a very difficult problem, and tend to strain on the lead, although monkeys and chimpanzees usually find the solution immediately.

A rather similar detour problem arises if food is placed on one side of a wire fence, and the animal on the other side must move away from the food to find a gap through which it can pass. The closer the food is to the fence, the more difficult is the problem for the animal. Kohler found that if a chimpanzee was standing close to a fence and food was thrown some distance away on the other side, then the chimpanzee had no difficulty in going round the fence to reach the food. However if the food was placed very close to the chimpanzee, but on the other side of the fence, the very nearness and attractiveness of the food prevented the chimpanzee from making the necessary detour to reach it.

Other more sophisticated problems might require the experimental animal to choose one of two doors depending on the patterns of earlier stimuli. A rat, for instance, may have to choose the left of two grey doors if it is preceded by a door with vertical stripes, and the right grey door if the preceding door has horizontal stripes. This sets up an 'if A – then B' response. Shepard tested for reasoning in rats by means of a complex maze in which one section could be removed. (see Figure 49)

FIGURE 49

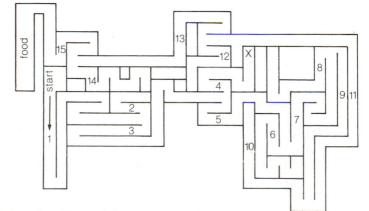

After the rats had used, and learned the maze, the wall marked X was removed, therefore causing a previous blind alley to become a short cut. Having discovered the change while running along the last part of section 11, and exploring a little from there into the end of section 4, some rats entered section 4 instead of section 5 on their next trial.

Some experiments tested the animal's capacity to discriminate between objects. Harlow showed a monkey two different objects, one of which either covered, or contained, food. After many trials with different pairs of objects the monkey learned to discriminate between new pairs very rapidly. With any particular pair the monkey had a 1 : 1 chance of hitting the right one at the first trial. If it did this, it subsequently went on choosing that particular object, irrespective of its position, throughout the rest of the experimental run. If, however, it chooses the wrong object it will immediately switch to the other one, and does not go back to the incorrect one. The first trial is an information run; having assimilated the information the monkey does not need to make trial and error reactions.

All of these are experimental situations, and it is difficult to extrapolate from the behaviour of animals with sticks and boxes to that shown by animals living under natural conditions. For a long time the fact that man was a tool making and tool using animal was a reasonable defining property, but it is now becoming clear that non-human animals can make and use tools in situations which require insight or reasoning. Wild chimpanzees will poke pieces of stiff grass into ant nests, and then lick off the ants which run up the grass. Miyadi has described a new behaviour pattern shown by a Japanese monkey, *Macaca fuscaca*, which was a member of a troop on Kojima Island. The monkeys fed on sweet potatoes put down for them, and one young female, instead of rubbing the soil off the sweet potatoes, washed them in a stream. This behaviour was copied by her mother and siblings, and within a short time by all the troop members apart from the old males.

These problem solving behaviour patterns suggest that some animals can put together elements from past experience, and can produce a novel, inventive solution which they can remember. Past experience is important; Kohler found that a chimpanzee with previous experience of handling sticks or boxes was much more likely to be able to solve a new problem. The animal must be able to store up information about past events and this information store is what we call the memory.

Various investigators have tried to localise the area of the brain involved in learning and the retention of the learned behaviour pattern. Lashley, in a classic series of experiments in the 1920s, studied the effects of brain lesions in rats on both new maze learning and the retention of already learned behaviour. He found that new maze learning was impaired in proportion to the extent of the damage to the cerebral cortex, but was not affected by the position of the lesion. Similar results were found with rats which had already learned the maze; the loss of learning was proportional to the extent, but was unrelated to the position, of the lesion.

Of course, such experiments cannot be carried out on human beings, and much of the evidence we have on the localisation of learning and memory in the brain comes from people who have suffered brain injuries. Damage to the left cerebral hemisphere has more effect, in general, on memory than damage to the right cerebral hemisphere. The two cerebral hemispheres are almost separated from each other by a vertical cleft, across which runs a broad band of nerve fibres called the corpus callosum. The presence of this band of fibres means that impulses can pass from one hemisphere to the other, so that both sides of the brain 'know' what information has come in. Because of the crossing of nerve tracts within the spinal cord, the right cerebral hemisphere receives impulses from the left side of the body, the left hemisphere being functionally connected with the right side of the body. Impulses coming in from the eyes however reach the brain through a slightly different arrangement. (Figure 50)

If someone learns to make a visual discrimination between two objects using only one eye, then he would have no problem in distinguishing the objects when using the other eye. Both sides of the brain have received the necessary information through the optic chiasma. Even if this optic chiasma were damaged or sectioned, information could still pass from one side of the brain to the other through the corpus callosum. However if this also were sectioned then the two sides of the brain would be isolated from each other and unable to pass information across. This drastic action has been carried out experimentally in man to alleviate a severe form of epilepsy. In this the abnormal firing pattern of the neurones spreads rapidly through the corpus callosum producing a very high frequency of 'grand mal' convulsions.

FIGURE 50

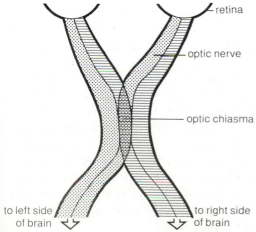

retina

optic nerve

optic chiasma

to left side of brain

to right side of brain

Arrangement of nerve fibres between the mammalian retina and the brain.
The optic nerves split into two sections at the optic chiasma. This means that nerve fibres from the left side of both eyes, and therefore carrying impulses from the retina of the right field of view, pass to the left side of the brain. Information of the left field of view will be received by the right side of the two retinas and will pass to the right side of the brain.

Although the decision to destroy or section any part of the human brain is not one to be taken lightly, the results of such an operation have been very satisfactory in improving the lives of patients who were previously completely incapacitated by their illness. Gazzaniga has investigated these post-operational patients who now have, as it were, two separate brains. In normal circumstances their behaviour seems entirely normal and unaltered by the operation, and both their sensory and motor systems function normally. However, in an experimental situation in which only one side of the brain receives information, some very interesting results were found. (Figure 51)

The left hemisphere could read words through the left eye and act on printed commands, either by speaking or by using the right hand to select named objects by touch. However the right hemisphere on receiving information from the right eye seemed unable to 'say' which word or picture it had seen, although it could choose the correct word from a set of printed words. It could also direct the left hand to search for, and select, the correct object even if it could not give it a name. The left hemisphere is relatively specialised for active word communication, whether by reading, speaking or writing, whereas the right hemisphere deals with the spatial relationships within and around objects, and with non-verbal reasoning. It has long been known that the effects of brain injury, whether by external accident or internal crises such as cerebral haemorrhages, depended on the position of the damage. A person with a haemorrhage or a thrombus on the left cerebral hemisphere will suffer from word difficulties.

Impulses reaching the visual cortex from the eyes are decoded during perception according to the information they hold, and also according to previously stored information. This being so, the brain tends to 'fill in' missing signals with what it expects to be present. (Figure 52)

FIGURE 51

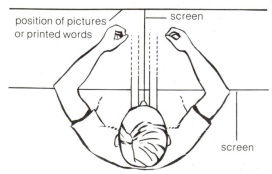

position of pictures or printed words
screen
screen

View from above of 'split-brain' subject, taking part in an experiment which gives information only through one eye. The subject can see objects in one section at a time, and acts upon instructions.

In figure 52, neither the 'white triangle' nor the word made of 'white letters' is really present; the brain extrapolates from the black areas to define the white in what seems to be the most sensible form.

Sometimes the brain cannot decide which of two possible alternatives is correct, and keeps switching from one picture to the other. (Figure 53)

It may be difficult to make the switch from seeing one picture to seeing the other one in figure 53; closing the eyes for a second or two usually helps.

So perception is not just the straightforward translation of incoming signals. Previous knowledge and experience can usually enable the brain to build up a complete picture from limited input; a proceeding which is based on the high probability that the object seen will be similar in form to one seen before.

FIGURE 52

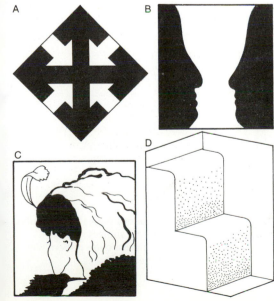

'Filling in' illusions.
The brain tries to make sense of the black shapes, and can do so best by seeing non-existent white shapes, which are either bounded by the black (the white 'triangle') or cast shadows to make the black shapes (the white 'letters').

FIGURE 53

A and B   In these two diagrams there is not enough information about whether the black or the white area is to be the background. So the brain alternates, sometimes seeing black arrows and two black profiles, and sometimes seeing white arrows and a white vase.
C   This figure can either be seen as an old woman looking to the left front, or as a young woman looking away.
D   The figure shows either the top or the lower surface of a staircase.

12 Memory and human learning

As we have seen, much of the evidence for the localisation of information in the human brain has come from brain damaged subjects. The split-brain technique has shown that the cerebral hemispheres appear to be centres which receive, utilise and store information. A certain asymmetry is apparent; the left hemisphere stores verbal, the right hemisphere non-verbal information. This view is supported by EEG work by Galin and Ornstein in 1972. An electroencephalograph or EEG is an instrument, developed by the German psychiatrist Hans Berger in the 1920s, which can record and printout electric currents originating within the brain, monitored by means of electrodes applied with conducting jelly to the scalp.

When a person is sitting with closed eyes in a relaxed state then the instrument records a series of fairly regular waves at about 10 cycles per second, making up what is called the alpha rhythm. Deep sleep reduces the frequency down to 1 to 3 cycles per second (the delta rhythm) whereas wakefulness and alertness increase both the frequency and the irregularity of the trace (the beta rhythm). (Figure 54)

FIGURE 54

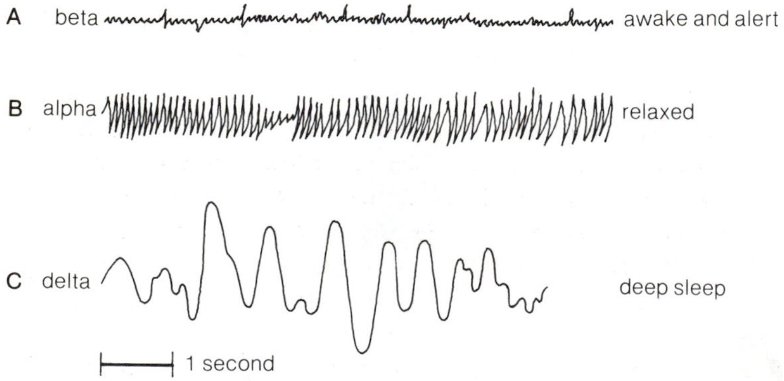

A   beta ⁓⁓⁓⁓⁓⁓ awake and alert

B   alpha ⁓⁓⁓⁓⁓⁓ relaxed

C   delta ⁓⁓⁓⁓⁓⁓ deep sleep

⊢——⊣ 1 second

Typical electroencephalograph patterns in wakefulness and sleep.
A A beta pattern appears when the subject is awake and alert.
B An alpha pattern of fairly regular waves at a frequency of 8–13 per second is shown when the subject relaxes.
C Deep sleep gives a delta pattern with much slower, deeper waves.

Galin and Ornstein found that when a person was working on a verbal task such as letter writing there was an asymmetry in the EEG trace. The left hemisphere showed the jagged, fast waves of attention, whereas the right hemisphere showed the slower, regular alpha rhythm. Visio-spatial tasks produced the opposite effect, with an alpha rhythm in the left, and a beta rhythm in the right hemisphere.

Information, whether verbal or non-verbal, which has entered the brain is stored within two different memory systems. In 1904 the German zoologist Richard Semon suggested that any stimulus received by an organism leaves a characteristic material trace within the nervous system, and this trace he called an 'engram'.

The first result of certain types of sensory stimulation is the formation, via sensory circuits, of a fleeting mental image which rapidly dies away. If twelve photographs are glimpsed at, then four or more may be recalled and named. The actual 'naming' of these images, that is the association of a word with the picture, seems to strengthen the memory of them, at least for a time. Sternberg, in 1969, carried out a series of investigations into the way in which the brain deals with new sensory information. A subject saw, or heard, a series of letters, one after the other, and was told to remember them if possible. A further letter was then given and the subject had to decide whether or not it had appeared in the series. The experiment was then repeated but this time nonsense syllables were substituted for the single letters. The time taken for the subject to mentally 'scan' the series and see if the new item fitted varied with the length and character of the series. The series of single letters was relatively easily remembered and scanning time was short. The more complicated the items in the series, the longer it took for the comparison to be made. The original series had been stored in what is called the short term memory which persists from a few seconds to a few minutes. If the series was made of complicated items like nonsense syllables it could take up more than the short term memory capacity. Part of it would then be shunted into a second system – the long term memory – and retrieval time would be correspondingly slower.

The short term memory may be very short indeed. One may look up a telephone number and have forgotten it again by the time one has finished dialling.

Items are held within the short term memory by being 'rehearsed'. In an experiment carried out by Peterson and Peterson subjects were presented with a single three letter nonsense syllable which they had to try to recall whenever a red light went on. They were also given a number such as 306 immediately after the nonsense syllable had been presented, and told to count backwards in threes – 306, 303, 300 and so on – and this prevented them from rehearsing the syllable. (Figure 55)

FIGURE 55

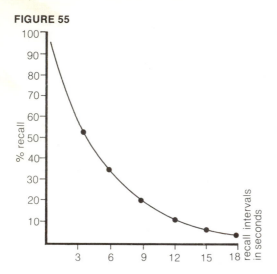

Experiment to show the effect of lack of rehearsal on memory. Subjects were asked to recall a previously given nonsense syllable at three second intervals, but had to count backwards in three's at the same time. This prevented them from 'rehearsing' the syllable, and recall scores dropped rapidly.

Based on Peterson.

The red light was flashed on every three seconds, and the recall scores dropped very rapidly; within three seconds about half of the subjects had forgotten the nonsense syllable.

When new material comes into the short term memory the original items are either passed into the long term system, or rehearsal of them ceases and they are forgotten. The importance which a subject may attach to certain items on a list, and therefore the attention given to them, can also affect the retrieval not just of those items, but also of other items. This effect was shown by Ellis in some investigations in 1971. Fifteen 'non-emotional' line drawings were shown, one by one for a constant short time, to subjects who were asked to remember them, in order, at the end of the experiment. A different set of drawings was then presented to the subjects, but this time a 'high priority' item (a nude photograph) had been placed half way through the series. (Figure 56)

As expected, in each series the later drawings were remembered better than the earlier as they were closer in time. The earlier drawings were remembered quite well as they were easier to 'pin down' into a serial position. However the 'high priority' item was remembered better than all the others. Items just before and after the 'high priority' item were remembered by fewer people. It appears that the attention given to the nude photograph had an amnesic effect on the less interesting drawings both before and after its appearance. It has been found that a monetary reward for remembering a particular item also wonderfully stimulates the memory.

The fact that certain items which seem to be important to the subject are preferentially remembered suggests that these high priority items, on being moved to the long term memory, are associated with a

FIGURE 56

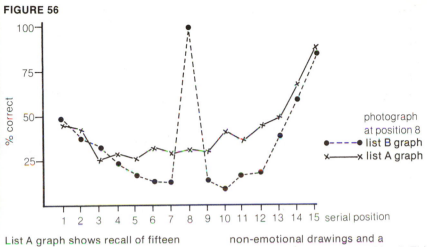

List A graph shows recall of fifteen non-emotional line drawings. The later drawings were remembered best by the subjects, as would be expected. List B graph contained fourteen non-emotional drawings and a photograph of a nude at position 8. This was remembered by everybody, but recall of items at serial positions on each side of it was diminished.

change of some permanence within the nervous system, and this would appear to agree with Semon's idea of the engram. Part of the limbic system, a composite structure which lies within the temporal lobes and near the thalamus, seems to be involved particularly with short term memory. This is the hippocampus, which enables us to select for notice what is important. People with slight hippocampal damage find it difficult to concentrate – their thoughts are interfered with by irrelevancies. Greater hippocampal damage may result in a complete lack of a short term memory system. Such patients may read, with enjoyment, the same page of a magazine over and over again, and immediately forget the name of someone who has just been introduced to them. It is the short term memory which is impaired on ageing. Many old people can remember clearly what they did at school seventy years before, but not where they last left their spectacles.

Many investigators have searched for physical patterns and arrangements within the brain which would permit or cause the retention of information. An examination of the cerebral cortex of man, or the octopus optic lobes, shows numerous 'self-exciting' or reverberatory circuits in which neurones are arranged in such a way that impulses passing along their axons are eventually conducted back to the cell bodies. It was thought that there is continual electrical activity within these circuits, that the impulse becomes trapped within them, running round and round to form the memory trace, but experiments carried out by Andjus on rats and Glees on monkeys have suggested that this is not the correct explanation. In these experiments the anaesthetised animals were cooled to a temperature when all electrical activity, as monitored by EEG readings, ceased within the brain. Even after a period of time at the low temperature there was no apparent loss of long term memory when the animals were warmed up and revived. Although continuous circular transmission of impulses does not appear to explain the functioning of the memory trace, it is possible that either the passage of an impulse along a particular pathway facilitates future transmissions, or that other unwanted transmission paths are inhibited. J. Z. Young has postulated such a system to explain the experimental results in the octopus and the crab situation mentioned in Chapter 10. (Figure 57)

Certain cells within the octopus brain, classifying cells, react to a particular visual contour. Each cell can originally stimulate either attack or retreat, but the results of the action, that is food or pain, send signals to the memory system which inform it of the 'correctness' of the response. The hypothesis is that the signals reach the memory system through small cells which can produce inhibitory substances which block the unwanted response.

Experiments with cats suggest that such classifying cells responding to particular visual contours are present. When an image of a particular form, such as a square, falls on the retina impulses pass to the visual cortex. Here, in the adult animal, there are nerve cells which respond to lines of particular orientation of the retinal image. So some cells would respond to vertical, and some to horizontal lines. (Figure 58) Blakemore and Cooper kept kittens in the dark except for periods in which they were exposed either to vertical or to horizontal stripes, their view of their own body being prevented by a wide collar. When the kittens matured they reacted to the visual orientation they had already met, but apparently did not see lines of other orientation. Blakemore and Cooper suggested that the visual cortex cells had adjusted to the visual experience of the kitten. So cells which would, in normal circumstances, have become sensitive to horizontal or diagonal lines would now respond to vertical lines in a cat reared with vertical stripes only. Other workers agree that such experiments lead to a situation in which the cortical cells respond to a particular orientation, but think that this results from the loss, through lack of use, of the other cells.

Such experiments link up what we may consider to be memories of previous stimulation with actual changes in the functioning of individual neurones.

Much of the recent work on memory deals with the biochemical changes which occur during the consolidation of memory traces. If neurone circuits are being established and neurones are active, then one would expect increases in the concentration of the enzymes which

FIGURE 57

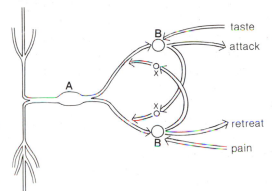

A   classifying cell
B   memory cells

It is suggested that classifying cells within the octopus brain record a particular visual contour. These cells initially make the octopus attack or retreat.

In the situation described in Chapter 10, the octopus would carry out its normal pattern of attack the first time the crab is presented with a white square. This behaviour, however, would lead to pain from the electric shock. Pain impulses reach the memory cell and bring about retreat, but the collateral nerve fibre from the memory cell carries impulses from it to the small cell (x in the diagram). This inhibits the attack pathway. The classifying cell would then always produce retreat when the white square appears.

Based on Young.

FIGURE 58

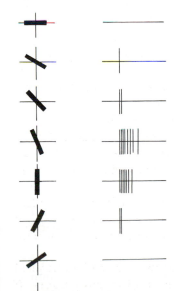

position of line   firing response of nerve
shown to cat   cell in the visual cortex

Hubel and Wiesel's results from an experiment in which they monitored the activity of a single cell in the visual cortex of a cat. A line, the solid bar on the left of the figure, was presented to the cat in the positions shown. The lines on the right of the figure show the firing response of a single cell in the visual cortex. This particular cell does not respond to horizontal lines.

Based on Hubel and Wiesel

synthesise and break down neurotransmitters such as acetyl choline. However during such consolidation more protein is made than is needed for the transmitter enzymes. As proteins are made in cells through the influence of RNA, it might be expected that the RNA concentration in actively transmitting neurones would also increase and various types of experiments have been carried out to investigate this.

In one series, substances which speed up or slow down the synthesis of nucleic acids were injected into animals, and their subsequent ability to learn new tasks, or to remember old ones, was then examined. Dingman and Sporn trained rats to pass through a maze, and then injected them with an analogue of guanine. This became incorporated into 'RNA' which, as it did not contain guanine, was not a meaningful code. This had no effect on the rats in further trials in the same maze, and so had not affected their memory of it. If the guanine analogue was injected before rats were placed in a new maze, then the injected animals appeared to learn it more slowly than control rats. However in different experiments Barondes and Jarvik found that learning could proceed normally in animals in which brain RNA synthesis was inhibited by actomycin D. In further experiments, Barondes found some agreement with Dingman and Sporn's results. He injected cyclohex-imide, a potent inhibitor of cerebral protein synthesis, into mice some time after they had been trained to perform a simple task and found that it had no effect on memory. If the cycloheximide was injected before training it also appeared to have no effect on learning. However although memory appeared to be normal for the first three hours after training, there was then a rapid decline in memory compared with control mice. This would suggest that cerebral protein synthesis is not needed for learning, but is very important in consolidating long term memory.

A second type of experiment involved analysing particular regions of the brain for nucleic acid and protein concentration and composition after a specific task had been learned by the animal. Hyden was able to demonstrate a change in the bases of the RNA in some rat brain cells which seemed to be associated with learning. The RNA was extracted from particular brain cells and it was then hydrolysed. The resulting free bases were separated by electrophoresis and their proportions determined. In the experiment rats were trained to walk up wires to food, the wires being at a 45° angle to the ground, and the RNA in their brain stem cells was found to be different, with an increased amount of adenine and decreased uracil, from that found in untrained rats.

The third series of experiments has had more publicity although the results have not been conclusive. The basic experiment involves training animals to perform a particular task, killing them, extracting their RNA or proteins and injecting these into untrained animals. The main proponent is J. McConnell who trained planarians to associate the flashing of a light with an electric shock, killed them, ground them up and fed them to untrained planarians. These 'cannibal' planarians learned a similar behaviour pattern much more quickly than untrained worms. Other scientists were sceptical. The Journal of the American Medical Association asked – 'Want to be intelligent? Swallow a professor!' The debate about the chemical transfer of learning is still going on. It has proved very difficult for McConnell's results to be replicated by other researchers in other laboratories. Even with planarians, which are the simplest animals used in chemical transfer experiments, there are many known variables which need to be standardised: the species and source of the worms; the kind of training they receive; the amount and type of food given; the ion concentration of the surrounding water; the condition of the trough; the light sensitivity of the worms.

Researchers who believe that chemical transfer of learning can occur are divided amongst themselves as to whether RNA, a protein or some other molecule is responsible. Ungar has isolated a short chain polypeptide, which he has named scotophobin, and which he claims transfers a fear of the dark from a rat trained to associate darkness with an electric shock to a naive mouse.

There are theoretical problems involved in understanding how chemical transfer could occur. Any molecule which is specific for a particular segment of learned behaviour must have the information encoded within it. This coded molecule must then be able to pass from the point of input, whether it is through the gut or more directly into the blood stream, to the brain with the code intact. It must then arrive at the correct brain circuit for that type of behaviour and be incorporated without changing its form.

It looks as though we shall have to wait some time before the question of chemical transfer of learning is solved. There is still a long way to go before the pharmaceutical industry could produce 'learning pills'. The cups of black coffee in the small hours of the night will be with students for a long time yet. However although we may have to wait until the twenty-first century for 'learning pills', there has been a revolution in learning methods during the present century.

During the 1920s Pressey developed a device which he called a 'Tester-Rater'. The student was presented with a printed sheet of numbered questions in multiple choice form, and also with a 'punch board' containing a matrix of holes which were arranged in rows for the question numbers, and columns for the possible answer choices. Behind this 'punch board' a piece of paper was placed, and behind this was a further sheet with holes in the correct places for the given questions. When the student had decided on his answer he pushed a metal stylus through the appropriate hole. If he was correct, the stylus passed through the paper making a hole, which allowed his answer to be scored, and then through the hole in the backing board. If in the wrong hole, the stylus stopped at the paper. The student therefore knew immediately if he had answered correctly and could move on to the next question. If he had answered incorrectly he could carry out a trial and error technique and find the right answer.

Skinner extended Pressey's work by applying his knowledge of shaping techniques which could be used to modify animal behaviour patterns. He concentrated on the form of the lesson, which was a programme of instruction in which the student had to answer one question before proceeding to the next. The correct answer could be read with the next question and so reinforcement of the behaviour pattern was almost immediate. The programme could be in a specially devised work book, or be in a teaching machine, but the style of programme is similar. The early questions in a programme are usually very easy, and so reinforcement for correct answers occurs. The student is not therefore in the common situation of waiting for a week or more to find out if the previously handed in work is correct. Skinner believes that positive rather than negative reinforcement is more effective with human learning, and so it is important that the programme proceeds by small steps as this reduces the student's chance of making errors. Such a linear programme can lead the student by small, easily assimilated steps to a good understanding of difficult concepts. (Figure 59)

In some cases, however, the very smallness of the steps can become tedious to a bright student. Crowder devised a system in which a student can proceed at a fast rate if correct, or can take a remedial 'branch line' if a mistake is made. This type of branching programme is used in the Auto Tutor Mark II teaching machine. (Figure 60 page 110)

In this a filmed programme is shown on the screen. Each frame gives a paragraph or two of information and often a diagram. A question is phrased in multichoice form and the student presses the appropriate button to the right of the screen. If the answer is correct, then the film rapidly moves on to the next step in the lesson. If the wrong button is pressed, the next frame presented will contain information to correct the error.

Just as with linear programmes, branching programmes can be arranged either as a film in a teaching machine, or in book form. The books are more open to 'cheating' and leaping ahead, but are considerably less expensive. However the very nature of the machine, with its button pressing, appeals to some students, and so is reinforcing in itself.

FIGURE 59

Programme on Sense Organs.
Cover the right hand column with a strip of paper.
Fill in the blanks before moving on to the next
statement.

1   Organisms can respond to the outside world or
    what is called their _____.   environment
2   Their 'knowledge' of the environment is gained
    through a particularly _____ part of the
    organism.   sensitive
3   Such a sensitive part may be within a single
    cell as in the protists, or may be in cells
    scattered over the surface, or in cells gathered
    together to form special _____ organs.   sense
4   Sensitive cells, whether scattered or in special
    sense organs, are _____ by some change in
    the environment.   stimulated
5   On being stimulated they respond by passing
    on information to other parts of the _____.   organism
6   In single celled organisms the information
    passes through the cytoplasm of the cell; in
    multicellular organisms the sensitive cells are
    connected to the _____ system.   nervous
7   The energy of the stimulus is converted into an
    _____ which passes through the nervous
    system.   impulse
8   The impulse is generated because of a change
    in the membrane of the sensitive cell. When the
    cell is stimulated there is a change in the ionic
    relationships of the cell membrane and this
    produces a local _____ charge.   electric
9   This local electric charge is called the
    generator potential, and if it builds up to a
    certain value called the threshold value, then
    an _____ will pass along the nerve fibre.   impulse
10 If stimulation continues then the first impulse
    will be followed by a second impulse, and so
    on. If stimulation is strong, many impulses will
    be generated; if stimulation is weak _____
    impulses start.   few
11 If stimulation continues there may be a falling
    off in the number of impulses passing, and
    eventually they may stop altogether. This is
    called sensory adaptation, and the time taken
    for it to occur depends upon the type of
    _____ involved.   sense organ
12 Some sense organs like those responding to
    touch in the mammalian skin adapt very
    quickly; others adapt slowly or not at all, like
    the auditory cells in the ear.

The present rapid expansion of microprocessors is likely to lead to the development of much more sophisticated teaching machines, and it seems likely that programmed learning will play an increasing part in our educational system.

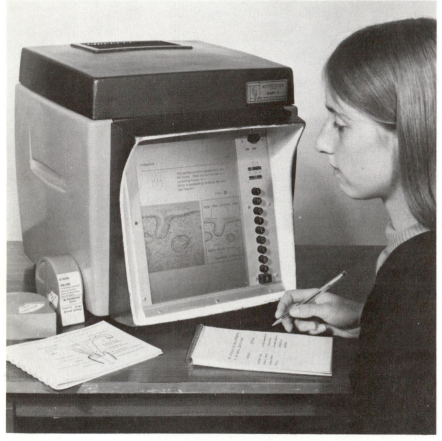

FIGURE 60
The AutoTutor Mark II Teaching machine.
This is a fully branching teaching machine using programmes on 35 mm film.

Courtesy of ESL (Bristol) Ltd.

13 Aggression

We know what we mean by 'fear' and 'anger'; these are subjective states which we can recognise within ourselves and which we assume will produce the same conscious sensations in other people. In animals other than man, however, we can only assume that certain behaviour patterns such as retreat or fighting are correlated with fear and anger.

An animal can react to painful stimulation by spinal reflexes to withdraw the injured limb even when its brain has been completely removed. If the brain stem is left intact with the spinal cord the response is more widespread, with general struggling or crying out; if the hypothalamus is also left intact then the experimental animal responds with rage, rather than withdrawal. Rage responses in such an animal will also occur on quite trivial stimulation, and it seems that the hypothalamus is normally restrained by the higher parts of the brain. Lesions in the hypothalamus of cats produce aggressive behaviour, a normally docile animal turning on anyone who touches it. Electrical stimulation of the hypothalamus by means of electrodes produces sham rage.

Other regions of the brain are also involved in fear and anger responses. Lesions in the amygdala, which is part of the limbic system, seem to induce a loss of caution in monkeys; the monkeys do not carry out the normal pattern of retreating when approached by people. Delgado in 1970 reported some work with a young aggressive chimpanzee called Paddy. Electrodes were implanted within the amygdala and a characteristic firing pattern occurred when Paddy behaved aggressively. These signals were then fed through a transmitter into the brain stem where they apparently led to discomfort. The chimpanzee quickly learned the connection between his 'angry' feelings and the discomfort, and gradually learned to control his amydgala. Such brain stimulation has been used to control behaviour in other animals, as Delgado himself had demonstrated in 1967 when he allowed a bull (in the brain of which he had previously planted electrodes) to charge him in the bullring. When he pressed the transmitting button, the bull was stopped just two yards away from him.

In the USA Mark and Ervin have used similar techniques in treating patients who have uncontrollable attacks of rage which otherwise would mean their isolation from other people. The part of the brain responsible for the unrestrained aggressiveness was found by brain stimulation by electrodes. Once located, the tiny region was destroyed and the tendency to violence disappeared. Such operations have also been reported in Japan, India, Mexico, France and Denmark. Sometimes instead of using electrodes just to locate hyperactive brain areas, electrodes are implanted so that the particular region can be regularly stimulated. In some cases aggression has been reduced; in others brain stimulation has been used to prevent epileptic seizures, or to bring relief from misery to patients with severe long lasting depression, or from the pain of terminal cancer.

Fear and anger responses at the right level and at the right time are of great importance in enabling animals to survive through numerous potentially dangerous situations. The anger responses may take different forms which may be classed together under the term aggression. Wilson has suggested one classification of aggression, although other writers may use different groupings.

1 Territorial aggression.
Many animals, including nearly all the vertebrates and some of the more advanced invertebrates, live out their lives under precise rules of land tenure. Each animal, or group of animals, occupies a particular area at a given time and this area, or territory, is maintained by the repulsion of intruders. Animal territories are not necessarily fixed like county boundaries on a map. As we have seen, in the three spined stickleback territorial behaviour may depend upon a combination of external and internal conditions, and therefore the territory may exist only at a particular season. However as long as the male stickleback is in his reproductive phase he will be aggressive to any other male intruder. Territorial aggression usually involves dramatic sign stimuli which are recognised by other animals. As we have mentioned earlier, the red belly acts as an aggressive signal to intruding males. Tinbergen observed that even a red mail van passing the laboratory windows posed a threat – all the reproductive male sticklebacks in the aquaria rushed at the glass and followed the van from one corner of their tanks to the other.

An accidental intruder has a repertoire of submissive gestures which enable it to leave a territory without further physical damage, and female birds frequently use elaborate appeasement signals to convert the male's aggressive displays into courtship.

2 Dominance aggression.
Dominance aggression displays may look very similar to territorial displays, but the result is not necessarily the driving of another animal out of the territory. Instead the dominant individual acquires a larger share of a particular necessity which may be in short supply. This could be many different things such as food, a mate, a sleeping area or a

displaying ground, but the net result is that the dominant animal will reproduce more often, and more effectively, than the others, and thus ensure the perpetuation of its genes. In mammals the dominant individual is characterised as much by special dominance signals as by its overtly aggressive behaviour.

3 Sexual aggression.
In some animal species a male will threaten and attack females to ensure mating. The male hamadryas baboon starts a harem with young females, and then harasses and bullies them all their lives to prevent them from straying.

4 Parental disciplinary aggression.
Many mammalian parents show aggressive behaviour patterns towards their offspring. A quick paw tap will break up fights or urge the young into movement. Such aggression leads into the next type.

5 Weaning aggression.
A conflict of interest arises during the suckling period. Mammalian young are completely dependent upon the mother for food in the early stages of their lives, but gradually their diet becomes more varied. Frequently the offspring will continue to beg for milk even though it no longer strictly needs it, and then the mother reacts with what has been called the 'flipping kids syndrome'. She will forcibly, and not always gently, remove the offspring from the nipple, and ignores the cries which earlier induced retrieval behaviour in her. We shall return to parent/offspring conflict in a later chapter.

6 Anti-predatory aggression.
Sometimes animals which normally behave defensively in the face of predation will, by means of concerted action, become aggressive. This is seen very clearly in 'mobbing' attacks where small birds will group together to attack a bird of prey such as an owl.

It is clear from this classification that aggressive behaviour differs in its extent and its functions. The disciplining of the young by a parent is very different from the competitive situation where adults fight for a territory or a resource, and the term 'agonistic' behaviour has been introduced to cover all aspects of fighting activity. Fighting between members of the same species is almost universal in vertebrates, although many of the fights have been highly ritualised. Young carnivores spend an appreciable amount of time in pseudo-fights, playful sparring in which they stalk each other, charge and pounce, but do not usually bite.

The pattern of agonistic behaviour varies from species to species, and is basically innate. Eibl-Eibesfeldt reared male Norway rats in isolation from the age of seventeen days to five months. An intruder rat was then placed in the cage. At first the isolated rat approached the intruder, and then it went into the complete species-specific display; it arched its back, gnashed its teeth and made high pitched cries. The two rats then wrestled, standing on their hind legs, and fighting often stopped at this point with one rat withdrawing. Sometimes proceedings went further into biting attacks. The fundamental pattern was the same in the isolated rat as in those rats which had been reared in a group.

Sometimes aggression 'spills over' into attacks on other uninvolved animals or even inanimate objects. Two rats which had been trained to fight each other were placed in a box in which there was also a small plastic doll. The rats ignored the doll and carried on fighting. As soon as one rat was removed however, the remaining rat attacked the doll. Such displaced aggression was also shown in an experiment in which a pigeon which had been trained to expect food when it pecked at a disc, was 'frustrated' by not receiving any. Another pigeon standing by was then vigorously attacked by the deprived bird.

Displaced aggression is also seen in human relationships. A man who is complained at by his superior at work, comes home and shouts at his wife, who then grumbles at the children. A child who has been smacked for being naughty goes off and pulls the cat's tail, or beats her doll.

It has long been thought that animals other than man always use their range of submissive and appeasement gestures to 'call off' a fight, and so it is extremely rare for real injury to occur. Man was considered to be the only species in which fights to the death were common or usual. However more and more evidence is accruing which shows that intra-specific killing is common in many other species. In lions, various types of monkeys and hyenas, fights between males can end in death. Infanticide is frequently seen. Male lions which have fought for, and taken over, a group of females will kill any young cubs – a strategy which ensures that their own genes will be passed on to the pride, rather than those of the ousted male. Young black headed gulls which wander from their parental nest territory are killed by neighbouring adult birds. Mother hyenas need to stand guard over their offspring at a kill to prevent them from being killed and eaten by other adult members of the group.

There are natural evolutionary limits to the level of aggression shown by organisms, however. If aggressiveness is genetically determined, then the 'aggression producing' alleles which have a phenotypic effect in a super-aggressive animal are also likely to be present in its relatives, but may be hidden in a heterozygous condition. If these relatives are attacked and their survival or reproduction rates are lowered, there will be a general tendency to reduce the frequency of the 'aggression producing' alleles in the population. Super-aggressive individuals also spend more time in maintaining their dominance positions or their territories and so the time available for reproduction is correspondingly reduced.

14   Territorial behaviour

It is obvious from the last chapter that one of the main types of aggression shown by animals is used to defend a territory. Most animals have to adapt to the fact that the available space must somehow be shared between them. These problems do not arise for those organisms which have no control over their own movements. Planktonic invertebrates, for example, are too small to do other than be carried around in water currents – they feed or are eaten, reproduce and carry out all their biological processes in regions which they do not choose.

However, in most cases organisms can select particular areas of a habitat, and so it is likely that those animals which, by some means, acquire a particularly useful area will strive to keep it.

Just as man recognises various levels of importance in his relationships with others (his immediate family; other people in his town or village; his country) other animals also have a graded series of interaction levels.

The area which an animal will cover during its whole lifetime is called the total range. Some parts of this may be intimately known and carefully learned, whereas other parts may be visited only once or twice. Within this total range there is a region, the home range, which is habitually patrolled and which may have sight or scent posts at its extremities. The home range and the territory may be synonymous, but in most species the home range includes land used for food gathering but not necessarily defended. A territory is an area occupied relatively exclusively by an animal, or a group of animals such as a family, and maintained by overt aggressive acts or signals. The term 'territory' was first used by Moffat in 1903 in describing the behaviour of robins, and most of the early work was on various species of birds. Now territorial behaviour has been studied in all the major groups of vertebrates and in several invertebrate phyla.

Sometimes a large area may be defended in which an animal may shelter, gather food, court, mate and nest, as in many species of small mammals, and in this case the territory is the same as the home range. A similarly large area may be used for breeding, but not for food gathering, as in the reed warbler. Many other birds defend only a small area around the nest, and sometimes territories are used just for pairing and mating.

Whichever system is adopted, however, there are advantages to be gained from territorial behaviour.

The population is spread out in relation to the available amount of food. The territory of a bird of prey may be a mile square, whereas that of a robin may be just one small garden. The amount of food available affects the population density and this is reflected in a variation of territory size. When food is scarce it is likely that there will be fewer animals in the population and this means that each animal can acquire a larger territory. Julian Huxley compared such a variable territory to an elastic disc which could expand and contract. The owner is safest at the centre where, of course, there will be fewer occasions to repel stray intruders. The centre is often the geometric centre, but sometimes it is the nesting site, or a point where there is more food.

A second advantageous result from territorial behaviour is to give the animals freedom from disturbance during pair formation. For many animals the amount of land available for territory claiming is severely restricted by the nature of their habitats. Many sea birds must mate, nest and rear their young on cliff ledges where territories may be measured in a few square feet, and in such conditions it is necessary that this small region is recognised and not intruded upon by other birds. The alteration of hormone balance which occurs during courtship and reproduction alters the type of territorial behaviour in many animals, as we have seen in the three spined stickleback. Both the great tit and the chaffinch mark out a preliminary territory by song and by fighting around selected display posts. Later when there are nestlings to feed their aggressive behaviour extends to their entire territory, and so gives greater protection to the family.

The spacing out of animals or family groups also reduces the chance of epidemic disease eliminating whole populations. A high population density makes the animals more easily found and attacked by predators, and the superabundance of prey enables the predators to increase their reproductive rates.

Territorial behaviour tends to follow a typical pattern. It is most usually found in adult males, which mark out a display area by some means. The display serves both to repel other males and to attract females, and the behaviour patterns are frequently the most elaborate ever performed by the animal. Territorial fighting may be fierce, but commonly it is avoided by different types of threat displays, and the equipment needed to carry them out is often confined to adult males. The claw of the fiddler crab, the antlers and horns of ruminants, the full throated roaring of bulls, lions and deer, and the less raucous sounds of bird song are all aggressive signals from one male to another which are recognised as territorial threats. Sometimes the signal is still part of an actual threat as in antlers, or the large canines of dogs; often it acts only as a signal, as in the red belly of the stickleback.

The actual detail of territorial behaviour differs from one species to another.

Territoriality in the laboratory mouse, *Mus musculus*, was investigated by MacKintosh who used an enclosure approximately two metres square which was divided into two sections by a partition. Groups of male mice were placed on each side of the partition and left for a week. During this time a hierarchy was formed in each group, a dominant male becoming established in each section. When the partition was removed the dominant male on each side defended its own area. If a mouse moved into the territory of another it was immediately attacked and chased over the invisible boundary line. This, of course, meant that the chaser had now become the intruder, and so the tables were turned and he was chased back. This boundary behaviour lasted for up to two months in the absence of the partition. Experiments with mixed, rather than all male, groups showed that female and juvenile mice did not elicit aggressive behaviour in the males which did not regard them as territorial rivals. Subordinate males moved very little as by this means they could avoid territorial confrontations.

Laboratory studies such as these are useful for observing behaviour in animals like mice which are difficult to watch in their natural environment. Most of the information we have on territorial behaviour however has been gained by patient, frequently physically uncomfortable, observations of birds from hides.

Lack studied robins from 1934 until his death, and published his findings in the classic book 'The Life of the Robin'.

Robins are fiercely territorial birds, a fact which Christmas card artists tend to ignore when they depict three or four robins sitting contentedly on a snow-covered bough. There is very little of the year in which the birds are neither acquiring nor maintaining territories.

The moult occurs in July and August, and the adult birds then keep themselves inconspicuous. In late July the young birds are beginning to acquire their red breasts, and they sing and fight sporadically. By early August both male and female adult birds are again developing red breasts and are becoming pugnacious; singing begins again and chases become more common. Late August sees more singing by both male and female birds, and individual territories are now claimed by adult and juvenile birds. The female leaves her territory in mid December to join a male in his, and from then on the joint territory is maintained by both birds. Nest building starts in March, and aggressiveness begins to decline by the end of May. Often two pairs may then be seen gathering food for the nestlings within the same area. Therefore territorial behaviour is seen for all the year apart from June, July and the early part of August.

Territories are preserved by a number of behaviour patterns. Within the territory the birds sing, display and make themselves conspicuous; outside it they are silent and do not display. If an intruder enters, the territory owner flies at it, often with very high pitched singing, and this is usually enough to drive the intruder out. If it stays, then the owner stops on a branch a short distance away and displays. The red breast is placed in as obvious a position as possible. Experiments with stuffed robins have shown that it is the redness that matters, as we have already mentioned in Chapter 7. (Figure 61)

During the display the bird slowly turns from side to side, and often holds the head and tail up. The wings may be flicked open and the crown feathers erected. The female carries out the same territorial displays as the male.

Tinbergen has made detailed studies of many birds, including the herring gull, *Larus argentatus.*

At the reproductive season pairs of birds are formed by reaction chain activity, each bird's behaviour acting as a stimulus for the behaviour of the other. Once the breeding pair is formed the two birds

FIGURE 61

intruder bird

Threat postures in the robin.
The territory owner, on the left of the diagram, positions himself to make his red breast as conspicuous as possible to the intruder bird.

A Threat from a position above the intruder.

B Threat from a position to the side of the intruder.

C Threat from a lower position than the intruder.

Based on Lack

acquire a territory in which a nest is made by lining a shallow depression with grass and moss. Copulation occurs and the established male now becomes very aggressive towards intruders. Three kinds of threat are used.

The first ploy is the 'upright threat posture' in which the male stretches to its tallest with its bill pointing downwards and then proceeds to walk stiffly towards the intruder.

This can be followed by what appears to be inconsequential behaviour. The male will walk almost up to the intruder, and will then suddenly bend down and pull up the grass by its roots. Such behaviour has been thought of as displacement activity, to which topic we return later, but it is more likely to be redirected aggression. Aggression is obviously still present in the vicious way in which the grass is tugged out, and the birds behave as if they are afraid to peck each other and so use up their aggression on something harmless.

Sometimes the male and female birds act together against an encroaching pair by showing a third type of threat. In this the defender birds bend their heels, lower the breast and point their beaks down to make a series of pecking movements at the ground, throughout which they make a rhythmic hoarse cooing call.

The threats work; other birds usually understand their meaning and retreat, allowing the mated pair to get on with the business of rearing their family.

15 Social groupings

If you leave the curtains undrawn on a dark night, it is not long before you can hear the tappings of insects on the outside of the window pane. They have been attracted to the light in a positive phototaxis. Sometimes the tactic behaviour is so strong that it leads to their death, as with moths which fly into a candle flame. Similarly large numbers of starlings collect at roosting sites in parks or on buildings as the light goes in the evenings.

Both collections of organisms may seem to be similar, but there are important differences between the two. The insects arrive one by one, are likely to be of different species, and affect each other only by physical proximity. The starlings are all of the same species, they arrive almost simultaneously and their flight pattern shows that they really do react to each other. This is an example of social behaviour.

Animals exhibit all grades of sociability. Some appear to be completely solitary, living out their separate lives unaffected by other members of the same species. *Chlorohydra viridissima* in a pond, feeding by nematocysts and through its symbiotic relationship with *Zoochlorella*, reproducing by asexual budding and moving around independently, survives without any relationship with another Hydra. Other aquatic animals can also maintain a soltary life. Even sexual reproduction may involve no more than a shedding of sperm and ova into the water, the two parents never needing to meet. For terrestrial animals, however such indiscriminate shedding of sperm and ova will not work. The sperm and ova must meet in a watery medium, and this occurs inside the female. A mating process is therefore a necessity, and so all animals which reproduce sexually on dry land must come together and socially react during reproduction, no matter how solitary they may be for the rest of their lives.

What happens after the actual mating process varies enormously throughout the animal kingdom. In many insect species the mated female flies away to find a suitable place to lay her eggs. This may be on a food plant, as in the large white butterfly *Pieris brassica*, or in a carcase as in the blowfly *Calliphora*, or each egg may be laid on living potential food as we have already described for the digger wasp *Ammophila campestris*. The female then leaves and the offspring develop, living independent lives until they too reach the reproductive stage. However it is in other insect species, the bees, ants and termites, that the most rigidly determined social organisation occurs, and we return to these in the next chapter.

Sometimes the mating process is a prelude to a period of time in which the mated pair stay together to rear the offspring. In many species the offspring stay with their parents beyond the rearing time and so large family groups are set up. In these circumstances males are often driven out of the group as they become sexually mature, and then have to acquire mates and territories for themselves by fighting. In such a society, in contrast to the rigidly genetically determined societies of the social insects, there is much more scope for the animal to alter its position of importance. In Burchell's zebra, for example, a dominant male may control six females and their young, giving a herd of up to fifteen animals. All other males are aggressively excluded. Similarly a male hamadryas baboon at his physical peak may control a harem of about five adult females. He herds them and prevents them from straying or associating with other baboons. In both of these examples young bachelor males wait on the sidelines, eventually acquiring harems of their own.

Such a system of dominance levels is commonly found in social animals, and as we have already mentioned, the system is maintained by the aggression of the higher ranked individuals towards the lower. In some species there is an obviously linear relationship, and this has been called a peck order as it was originally described, by Schjelderup-Ebbe, in the domestic fowl. If two birds are placed in the same enclosure, there will be a great deal of squawking, feather ruffling and pecking. Within a short time one bird will have dominated the other, and thereafter they can co-exist without too much friction. The same situation will occur as soon as a group of chickens form a new flock, and a series of encounters will establish a dominance chain. A high ranking, A grade, bird will gain priority of access to food, nest sites and roosting places, and will enjoy freedom of movement, all because it can peck and intimidate all the other birds. A B grade bird can peck all except the A grade bird; the C bird can peck all except the A and B birds and so on. Right down at the bottom of the social order is a bird which is pecked by all, cannot peck any, and which has to get what food, or space, is available when the others have finished. Dominant cocks mate more than lower ranked males and so pass on their genes to more offspring. Dominant females may mate less than other hens because they display submissive and receptive gestures to the cocks less frequently, but as they acquire more food and better nesting sites than others they are more likely to rear their chicks. If breeders select for birds which lay more eggs, they are also likely to get more aggressive chicks.

Early man was, of course, just one of the socially organised primate species. Variation in sociability in primates is very wide, as would be expected in an order which ranges from the tree shrews on the one hand, to the great apes and man on the other. The ecological niches occupied range from herbivorous tree dwelling to omnivorous, bipedal ground living such as is found in man. In the gorilla, *Gorilla gorilla*, troops usually consist of a dominant silver-backed male ten or more years old, one or two black-backed younger males, about six females and the same number of juveniles. The organisation and nature of the troop depends partly on the idiosyncrasies of the silver-backed male. Dominance is correlated with age and size, and there is very little overt aggression, even against intruders. The 'King Kong' chest beating and roaring has very little resemblance to the real behaviour of this 'amiable vegetarian' as Schaller calls it.

The most socially advanced non-human primate is the chimpanzee, *Pan troglodytes*. Chimpanzee social groups are much more variable in composition than those of gorillas. Jane van Lawick-Goodall found that in the Gombe Stream Reserve 30% of the groups were mixed, consisting of males, females and young; 24% were of mixed females and offspring; 18% were of mature and/or adolescent males and females; 10% were unisexual groups and the rest were solitary individuals. Mothers retain their links with offspring well past weaning time; often there is a close association for up to six years. The males cooperate for hunting and also for sharing out the meat. Even a dominant male was seen to hold out his hand in a begging gesture for scraps from another chimpanzee which had killed a small baboon. Foraging parties which find a good food supply, such as some laden fruit trees, rush about excitedly making whooping calls which can be heard by other chimpanzees which then approach.

Chimpanzees vocalise freely. When they are relaxed they make soft grunts which also inform others of their position. They threaten subordinates by a soft bark, and threaten superiors, from a safe distance, by a louder bark. High pitched screams are a threat to another group, and a 'hoo' call is given when a strange object is encountered.

The repertoire of gestures is also extensive in chimpanzees. Raised arms with the hands then slapping downwards, and a bipedal swagger with very little forward movement are both threatening gestures to other members of the group. Dominance behaviour is well developed, a low ranking member giving way to a high ranking one if they meet on a branch or a path. The dominant male often leads the way during movement, but sometimes it may be in the centre of the troop. However, even here it instigates movement; when it stops, the rest of the party stops.

Although the situation within a chicken coop is man-made an unnatural, the social organisation of a peck order is found in many birds in their natural societies. Lorenz found that young jackdaws quickly hammer out a linear ranking system, but that this has subtle differences from that of the chicken coop. He found that, once the linear order had been established, aggression was shown only between close ranking birds. Number 4 might bully Number 6, but would ignore Number 12 in the hierarchy. It does at least give some protection to Number 12.

Dominance hierarchies which are not so rigid and linear are found in many mammal societies. As we have already seen, red deer males and females live in separate hierarchically arranged groups except at the rut. Then the highest ranking males challenge each other and fight to acquire as big a harem as possible.

In the wolf, *Canis lupus*, a new pack is formed when a mated pair leaves the group to produce a litter. As the family grows, separate linear dominance orders develop in the males and females, as in the red deer. The founding pair occupy the senior positions for some time, and the young establish their ranking order during their play fights. The rank order is reinforced when they are adult by a series of aggressive and submissive gestures. The very important chief male is deferred to by the others in a greeting ceremony in which they tenderly nip, lick and smell his mouth – a pattern of behaviour which is ritualised from the food begging actions of the puppies. Such a social organisation, in which submission to a dominant leader plays an important part, could have enabled early man to pre-empt the leader's position and so gradually convert the wolf into the domestic dog, *Canis familiaris*. (Figure 62)

FIGURE 62

Dominance gestures in the wolf.
A and B, facial gestures.
A Dominant wolf.
B Subordinate wolf.
The dominant wolf holds its ears forward and its snout up.
C, D, E and F, tail positions.

C Confident tail position shown by a dominant animal when meeting other wolves.
D Normal tail position.
E and F Submissive gestures by subordinate wolf.

Chimpanzees also cooperate in defending a group area by attacking intruders. Van Lawick-Goodall observed chimpanzees throwing stones, both underarm and overarm, at baboons which were disputing their access to food. Kortlandt and his fellow investigators placed a model leopard with a moving head in the path of a group of savanna dwelling chimpanzees. Immediately they saw it, the members of the group scattered, the females seizing and removing the young. Older males, however, soon returned and advanced on the model, throwing sticks at it, spear fashion. A film shown at the International Ethological Conference in 1967 showed that the first male to advance to close range turned to 'shake hands' with other males before proceeding alone. Eventually many of the males approached and prodded the model with sticks, and their hands and feet.

As we can see, audio-visual and tactile signals are important in maintaining social organisation in chimpanzees, and in the most advanced primate, *Homo sapiens*, they have acquired even more importance. Although man uses conceptual thought and language in order to maintain his society, a vast amount of information is passed from one individual to another by means of facial expressions and body posture. It is not necessary to be told when someone is furious; the 'black look' and frowning forehead have already got the message across. Most of the communication preliminary to forming a pair bond (in other words, falling in love) is non-vocal, and it is obvious that facial gestures and body postures are enormously important.

Audio-visual signals are also important in establishing and maintaining a dominance hierarchy. In man this is not so simple as a peck order, but has various ramifications and parallel lines. Human societies tend to differentiate into many kinds of highly organised subgroups, such as political parties, or clubs, or committees, with overlapping memberships. If one is a lowly ranked member of one society, one might well be highly ranked in another. Human dominance is not always achieved by threat; there seems to be a psychological capacity for social deference once the hierarchy is established. The outward signs of the hierarchy may be incorporated in such human 'extras' as clothing; uniforms are an almost universally understood authoritative signal. The white laboratory coats worn by doctors and other scientists seem to have the same effect, making other people more willing to accept the subordinate role.

Between 1960 and 1965 Milgram and other psychologists at Yale University carried out a series of experiments to test the mechanism of obedience and submissiveness in a sample of Americans. The randomly selected subjects were asked to help with an experiment to test the effect of punishment on learning. However the researchers were really carrying out a different experiment; to see how far the subjects would go in carrying out orders given by a more authoritative person when the orders were at variance with their normal patterns of 'decent' behaviour.

Two people had been trained in their acting parts; one was to be the impassive, firm, white coated scientist, and the other, a mild mannered middle aged man, played the part of the victim. The victim was strapped into an electric chair apparatus in one room, and the subject was placed in an adjoining room in front of what appeared to be a normal electric shock generator. This was, of course, a dummy but the subject was given a sample shock to show that the apparatus was genuine. Switches on the dummy generator were grouped under the headings 'Slight shock' up to 'Danger – severe shock', and the subject was told that these corresponded to 15 up to 450 volts. Within the mock experiment the subject had to give gradually increasing 'shocks' whenever the victim gave a wrong answer in a series of ten words which he was supposed to memorise. As the victim had been told never to give all correct answers, the subjects were forced to give increasingly powerful 'shocks' if they were prepared to follow the orders of the 'scientist' standing near them. Any subject who refused to continue with the experiment was termed 'defiant'; those who followed orders were labelled 'obedient'. In pre-experiment discussions the researchers had assumed that no one would go beyond the fourth of the nine shock graduations – 'Very strong shock'; in the experiment this estimate was found to be far off the mark. Of the forty subjects tested, all went beyond this point, and twenty-six went all the way to the 450 volts mark. The victim played his part, banging on the table and shouting when the 'shocks' increased in severity. The subjects reacted in various ways; some showed nervous smiling and laughter, which seemed bizarre; others trembled and groaned – but they still went on. In further experimental series different subjects continued to 'shock' victims on command with what Milgram described as 'numbing regularity'.

It was likely that the subjects had been taught from childhood that to hurt another person is morally wrong and, yet man's tendency to defer and to obey authority was sufficient to allow them to do something which they thought was causing extreme pain in another human being.

Such an experiment throws some light on the way in which 'decent' people will cooperate in extremely cruel conduct. Guards in a concentration camp see themselves as only carrying out orders, no matter how cruel are their effects. The psychologist Bettelheim, who spent some time as a prisoner in Dachau and Buchenwald, noted that some of the prisoners, if put in charge of their fellow prisoners, became as cruel as the Gestapo. They identified with their warders to the extent of altering their clothes to look like Gestapo uniforms. Anyone who can present a powerfully dominant personality can usually find followers willing to go along with him, as a demagogue instigating mob violence well knows.

As we have seen, dominance and submission may be established by fighting, but are just as likely to arise from dominance signals which are answered by submissive behaviour. Both the dominance and the submissive signals can become simplified and exaggerated in form and then we say that they are ritualised. Particular dominance/submissive gestures which strengthen the social bond are called ceremonies. Ritual submissive displays frequently expose the most vulnerable part of the animal in a way which would not happen in a normal fight. Thus a wolf will display its throat to its opponent, and a domesticated dog will lie on its back exposing its unprotected belly. The very vulnerability seems to 'defuse' the situation.

Sometimes during the course of an encounter one of the protagonists, torn as it were between attack and flight, will carry out what appears to be completely irrelevant behaviour. This is displacement behaviour – described by Lorenz as 'the performance of a behaviour pattern out of the particular functional context of behaviour to which it is normally related'.

Fighting turkeys, for example, will break off the fight to eat and drink, and other birds will preen themselves during fighting. Such actions can result from activity of the autonomic nervous system. Conflict situations produce skin blood vessel changes and hair erection, and these skin sensations may, in turn, elicit scratching or preening. Similarly autonomic induced dryness of the throat will stimulate drinking. Cormorants exhibit sham incubation during intervals of fighting, avocets adopt a sleeping posture by placing the beak under the wing.

Human displacement activities are seen in certain stressful situations. Seiss studied the characteristics of lecturers who, in the exposed and isolated position in front of an audience, cannot carry out the desired escape mechanism. Instead they adjust to the situation in one or other way. They may be extremely formal, and thus lessen contact between themselves and their audience. They may modify their exposed position by making asides to their listeners, or indicating their wish for contact by friendly smiling or telling little jokes. The tension usually leads them into displacement activities which may be based on body care patterns (scratching the head, bringing the open hand around the nape of the neck, stroking the chin or beard) or eating behaviour (biting or sucking pens, swallowing, chewing). Some human displacement activities are based on learned behaviour patterns, such as fondling a tie, holding the lapels of a jacket or fiddling with a pencil.

Displacement activities are seen either when two conflicting behaviour patterns, such as aggression and withdrawal, are elicited at the same time, or when a particular pattern is elicited but is prevented from running its full course, as when courtship does not end in copulation.

In these examples of hierarchies, the dominant animal maintains its position by fighting or by ritualised threat gestures. Such ritualised gestures may direct the movement of the group. In the hamadryas baboon, the dominant male controls troop movement by carrying out what has been named the 'swing step'. In this he lifts his tail, swings his buttocks from side to side and takes long rapid steps, all of which induce subordinates to walk behind him.

The position taken up by the dominant animal varies from species to species.

In zebra, the dominant male will lead the group to a water hole, but the dominant female leads away, the dominant male bringing up the rear. Wolves in a pack can be led by whichever animal happens to be in front, but the dominant male takes over during a chase. In domestic cattle moving freely, the dominant animal leads, but if movement is forced, low ranking individuals move first. Sometimes leading appears to have little to do with dominance relationships. Shoals of fish are led by whichever fish happen to be at the front. When the shoal turns, then the fish on that side become the new leaders. Even here, visual information is important. Blind fish cannot shoal, and a fish blinded in one eye can approach and line up with other fish on its sighted side, but not on the other. The fish maintain a constant geometric orientation to their fellows, heading in the same direction with their bodies parallel and with equal spacing from fish to fish.

This equal spacing is maintained by the preservation of a particular volume of free space around the animal, and this need for 'personal space' is widespread. Speeded-up films of people moving on fairly crowded pavements show how carefully each person strives to avoid encroaching on another's personal space. Each of us is uncomfortable if a stranger approaches too near, and would tend to back away to maintain the same distance between us. Rush hour commuter travel is stressful because it becomes impossible for us to preserve our personal space. Man, because he moves each day to vast conurbations, has to submit to very high local population densities for appreciable periods of time. We call it the 'rat race' but rats have ways in which they control their population densities.

Overcrowding in natural populations is countered by the available supply of food, and the amount of disease and predation, but the population size may be controlled even if these limiting factors do not apply.

Crowcroft and Rowe allowed a few pairs of mice to populate a four metre square enclosure, ensuring that there was adequate food and nesting material for all as the population size rose. An explosive population increase could have been expected, but after it had reached a density of 39 mice per metre squared the population levelled out. At this level the female mice had disorders of the reproductive systems and so the birth rate dropped. Calhoun carried out similar experiments with Norway rats in a much larger enclosure. To begin with, some males guarded territories, but as the population density increased only a few highly dominant males managed to retain them. A large part of the population gathered in certain parts of the enclosure, and here aggression was heightened and maternal behaviour was very disturbed. Litters were ignored or eaten; sometimes litters were mixed with other litters or not covered with nesting material, and infant mortality rose to 90%.

Both of these were experimental situations in which population densities had reached levels which would not occur in natural conditions. However investigations with lemmings have shown that aggression also increases with population growth in natural populations. Krebs measured the amount of fighting in a lemming population at Baker Lake, North West Territories in Canada between 1959 and 1962 by counting the number of wounded individuals. He found that the percentage of wounded lemmings changed from 35% while the population was increasing, to 55% at population peak and 19% when the numbers had declined.

As we have already mentioned in Chapter 4, stressful situations result in increased activity of the adrenal cortex, and this eventually leads to the diminution of reproductive capacity which, in overcrowded conditions, is usually enough to restore the *status quo*.

16 Social insects

Rigid patterns of social organisation have evolved in two orders of insects, which comprise all of the termites (the isoptera), all of the ants and the more highly organised wasps and bees (the hymenoptera).

The complicated social patterns found in all of these insects are similar in many respects. There is cooperation between many individuals in caring for the young, and an overlap of two or more generations within the society with the offspring helping the parents during some period of their lives. An obvious division of labour also occurs, reproduction being carried out by one or more fertile individuals whereas food gathering and defence are performed by sterile nest mates.

The evolution of a society with such clearly delineated roles and castes is thought to have passed through many stages. Possibly the first stage was a community of animals which cooperated to build a nest, but each animal then raised a brood separately. This could lead to a situation in which the broods are reared cooperatively, but each female still lays eggs at some time in her life. This communal arrangement could become more efficient if some members became non-reproductive, their labour therefore being available to carry out other communal tasks. It has been suggested by Michener that this is the evolutionary pathway to social living taken by bees, although a slightly different path has been suggested by Wheeler for termites, ants and wasps. Here it is possible that at the most primitive level a female cared for her brood almost until they became adults; if this period of care was extended then the mother could still be present when the brood matured. They could then assist with the rearing of any additional broods she might produce. If some of the offspring became permanent, non-reproductive workers, then the same caste situation would have evolved.

Once the species has become social it can advance in organisation by an increase in the numbers and the degree of specialisation of the worker caste. Correlated with this there is an improvement in the communication system by which the colony members coordinate their activity. Some of the most elaborate communication patterns in the invertebrates are found in the social insects.

Let us now consider one social insect in some detail. The honey bee, *Apis mellifera*, is thought to have originated in the African tropics, from where it colonised more temperate regions before it was cultivated by man. Its tropical origin meant that the queen could continue to reproduce throughout the year, and so very large colonies could build up, from which new colonies could be started by swarming. Large colonies also necessitated efficient food gathering over a wide area, and so a good information system needed to evolve.

There are three castes of honey bee. Both the queens and the workers develop from fertilised eggs and are therefore diploid. Queens are fertile, workers are sterile females and the difference between them depends on the way in which they were fed as larvae. The drones, or males, develop from unfertilised eggs, and so are haploid.

A colony which has just got through the winter usually consists of a single queen and about twenty thousand workers. The workers build small, hexagonal cells as long as they receive at least 0.1 microgram of queen substance every day (see Chapter 5). In late spring the production of queen substance falls, and the workers build a small number of large, ellipsoidal queen cells at the lower margins of the combs. The queen continues to lay diploid eggs in both the small worker cells and the larger queen cells, but the larvae which develop are treated differently by the workers. Those developing in the queen cells are continually fed on royal jelly, a rich secretion of the pharyngeal glands of young workers, whereas worker cell larvae get this rich food for only a few days, thereafter being fed on a mixture of honey and predigested pollen. During this time the status of the queen alters, her abdomen is reduced in size and she begins to behave in an agitated manner. The workers now show hostility towards her; she is pushed out of the nest and flies off with a large group of workers. This forms the prime swarm, and occurs just after the new royal cells have been capped. The swarming bees fly for a short distance from the nest and then settle on an aerial perch. From here worker scouts go to find a suitable site for a new nest, and when they return they inform the swarm by means of the waggle dance, to which we return later.

Meanwhile the workers remaining in the original nest are queen-less. They had already built drone cells into which the queen had laid unfertilised haploid eggs, and these develop into males. The first virgin queen emerges after a speeded up development due to a continual diet of royal jelly (a queen takes sixteen days compared with twenty-one days for a worker and twenty-four days for a drone). She then visits other queen cells, tears them open and stings her rival sisters. Sometimes the workers prevent her from breaking open all the cells, and she then begins to 'toot' – a peculiar sound which can be heard up to ten feet from the nest. The imprisoned queens reply by 'quacking', a sound which is lower in frequency and has a different pattern from the 'tooting' of the already emerged queen. If two queens do emerge at the same time, then fighting ensues and one queen is killed.

The emergent queen is now urged out of the nest by the aggressive behaviour of the workers, and she now flies away on her mating flight, being followed by the drones which are attracted by the queen substance she produces. Mating is quick and violent, the male dying because his genitalia have been torn out. The queen may make three flights a day for up to twelve flights, and during this period will collect enough sperm from different males to last a lifetime. She then returns to stay in the original nest, or just to collect enough workers to make a secondary swarm. If this happens then a second emergent queen will carry out mating flights and will return to take over the original nest. The function of the drone is purely reproductive; he plays no part in the collection of food or the defence of the nest, relying for these upon the workers. Any drones which remain in the nest in early winter are expelled by the workers, new males being produced the following spring. (Figure 63)

The workers enter upon a complex series of behavioural acts from the time they emerge as adults; a pattern which depends upon serial changes within their endocrine glands. The young workers clean the cells in the brood area and the honey comb and then they become nurse bees, feeding and grooming the larvae. At this time their pharyngeal glands are large and produce royal jelly. Gradually the pharyngeal glands decrease in size; the abdominal wax secreting glands enlarge

FIGURE 63

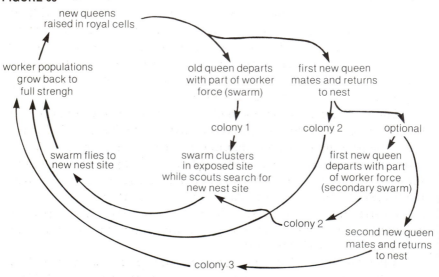

Swarming patterns in the honeybee.

Based on Wilson

and become active, and at this stage the worker can build new cells. After about a week of cell building the workers spend a few days storing pollen and receiving nectar from foragers. Guarding the nest from intruders (possibly carrying out suicidal attacks on persistent intruders) comes next in their programme of behaviour patterns. They regulate the nest temperature by exuding water for evaporation from their mouthparts, or by fanning with their wings. The last week of their short, thirty day adult life span is spent collecting food for the colony during foraging expeditions.

Most of this complicated behaviour is innate, although some learning is involved. A worker can learn the nest odour and also a nest mate odour, and can recognise intruders. She must be able to learn the position of the nest, or the position of the swarm, so that she can return to it. As we have seen in an earlier chapter, bees can be trained to react differently to different colour screens, turning to the right at a yellow, and to the left at a blue screen.

In order to convey information from one worker to another an efficient communication system is needed. The 'bits' of information which need to be passed might vary from an invasion warning to the precise location of food plants which have been found by scout bees, and the communication channel used varies according to the need. The amount of information needed to be given about an intruder is limited; a sound signal in a short, sharp buzz followed by the production of an alarm pheromone is enough to mobilise the nest. When a bee stings an intruder and then attempts to move away, the barbed sting with its poison gland, and also parts of the viscera, remain behind in the victim, and so the stinging bee dies. A pheromone is secreted by the glandular cells lining the poison gland reservoir. This pheromone which contains isoamyl acetate amongst other substances, quickly evaporates attracting other workers to the site of the battle.

Some information about a food plant is given by the odour on the body of the forager, and in the nectar carried back to the hive. To inform about the position of the food plant, however, needs a signal which is capable of pinpointing the plant by distance and angular references to some relatively fixed points. Such a signal is thought to be embodied in the waggle dance, decoded by Karl von Frisch in 1945.

A foraging worker returns to the nest, or to the swarm if it has been looking for a new nest site, and performs one of two dances in front of the other workers. (Figure 64)

They may be carried out on a horizontal or a vertical surface. The round dance gives no positional information except that the food is less than 100 metres away, although in the Egyptian honey bee this figure is reduced to 10 metres.

The waggle dance occurs if the food is more than 100 metres away and is a figure of eight in which the central straight run gives information about the direction of the food. In a vertical dance the angle at which the straight run is tilted from the vertical is the same as the angle between the sun, the nest and the food. In a horizontal dance the straight run points directly towards the food. However angular direction alone is not enough information; some idea of distance must also be given. During the straight run the worker waggles her abdomen 13–15 times a second and the actual speed of dancing is inversely related to the distance to the food. Average values taken from over six thousand dances show that the bee makes six complete dance circuits in fifteen seconds if the food is five hundred metres away, and this drops to two circuits if food is ten thousand metres away. (Figure 65)

FIGURE 64

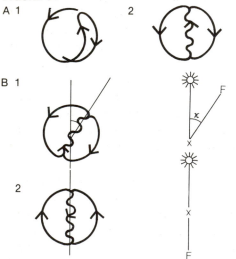

A1   The round dance, carried out by foraging worker bees. The bee follows the drawn path; this dance occurs if the food is within 100 metres of the nest.
2   The waggle dance. This is a figure 8 dance, the abdomen waggling taking place during the straight run.
B1   The straight run is tilted from the vertical according to the angle between the sun, the nest X and the food F.
2   In this case the sun, nest and food are in a straight line, and the straight run now points downward to show that the food is diametrically opposite to the sun.

FIGURE 65

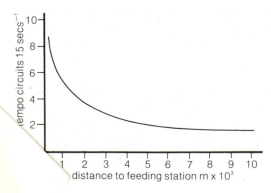

Graph to show the relationship between honey bee dance tempo (as measured by the number of circuits made in 15 seconds) and the distance between the hive and the food source.
The graph is based on average values from experiments carried out by von Frisch, Heran, Knaff and Lindauer, and involves over 6000 dances.

Based on von Frisch.

It has been shown, however, that bees incorporate information about the prevailing wind conditions into the dance. If a head wind is blowing against the bees on their journey to the food, then they dance more slowly, and this suggests a greater than actual distance. Similarly if the path to the food is up a steep slope, the apparent distance is increased. The dance, therefore, does not give an accurate estimate of distance, but does suggest the amount of energy that must be expended by the bee in reaching its goal.

Translated into human terms this would appear to be a reasonably efficient signalling technique. All that the other workers need to do is to watch the dance pattern, compute the angle and distance (or energy requirement) and then fly off to the food. However there are problems. There is very little light within the nest, and the dancing bee is surrounded by a large number of other workers and this disrupts the visual pattern. While the bee is dancing these other workers touch her thorax with their antennae, and this could allow them to sense the pattern of the dance. It would not, however, give them information about her waggling abdomen. Wenner has found that the dancing bee emits sounds of 250 Hz during her straight run, and these sounds could be picked up by the antennae of the surrounding workers, which have auditory organs. Sometimes returning foragers dance on the comb without making sounds. Esch investigated fifteen thousand dances and found that no silent dance led other bees to a food source. So it looks as if sound signals are also important in imparting information to recruit other workers to visit a food source.

Sound patterns are known to be important in many ways in honey bee colonies; at least ten different sounds have already been identified, including the queenly 'tooting' and 'quacking' we have already mentioned. Ventilating bees vibrate their wings at a particular frequency to control air movements in the nest. Guard bees produce a sharp buzzing noise while the emergency lasts, but then 'pipe' at 500 Hz at half second intervals, and this appears to calm the disturbed bees in the nest. Such a multiplicity of sounds would interfere with each other if they were to be received by the same sense organ, and there is some evidence that although the dance vibrations are perceived through the auditory organs on the antennae, other sounds are received through the legs of the workers.

So it is known that there are at least three informational systems available to the honey bee: odour, dancing and sound.

The controversy continues about their relative importance in natural, rather than experimental, conditions. If there is abundant food then the food odour within the hive may be so strong that the dance language is not needed. It is possible that the actual dance pattern is just an incidental accompaniment to a complicated sound production system. Honey bees are not unique in carrying out dance movements. If blowflies of the genus *Phormia* are fed sugar solution, they perform a kind of round dance, running in circles, and the speed of turning is proportional to the concentration of the sugar solution. The ladybird *Coccinella* will walk up a vertical plane in diffuse light if it has previously been walking towards a bright light along a horizontal plane. If the ladybird originally walked 30° to the left of the light source on the horizontal, it will walk at an angle of 30° to the left of upright on the vertical plane. As neither the blowfly nor the ladybird has a highly organised social life, informational 'meanings' for these movements have not been assumed.

It seems likely that bees use a combination of communication systems, depending on the circumstances which prevail at the time.

17 Courtship

As we have already mentioned, it is necessary for land animals to come together in a mating process for sexual reproduction to occur, even though the animals involved may be otherwise solitary. Obviously there must be some fundamental change in the organism which alters its normal solitary avoidance behaviour into a behaviour pattern in which it seeks contact with another animal. Even in animals which are social, changed behaviour patterns are needed to counteract the aggressive, dominance relationships and the preservation of personal space.

Reproductive behaviour is energy consuming, and also places the participants in a vulnerable, defenceless situation. It is important, therefore, that it is made as efficient as possible, and this efficiency can be considered from various aspects.

First of all, it must be synchronised in the male and the female. Sometimes the mutual performance of complex courtship patterns confirms that both partners are sexually receptive, and sometimes the female is brought to receptivity by watching the display of the male. If a male and a female pigeon are kept in adjoining cages so that, although they cannot mate, they can watch each other, then the male will display to the female and she will eventually lay eggs, which of course are infertile. Synchronisation can also occur by the type of reaction chain activity shown by the stickleback. In some cases the males carry out communal displays on special areas of ground called leks, and these high density displays attract solitary females. This occurs in various grouse species in which males collect and display to each other and also to any wandering females. The same type of lek system is found in some mammals such as hares, in which the males gather together in early spring and display to each other (so becoming mad, March hares) and these displays attract the females.

The courtship display may also be necessary to reduce aggressive behaviour in the male, or escape behaviour in the female. Occasionally courtship is needed to reduce aggressive predatory behaviour in the female. In spiders, for example, the males are generally smaller than the females, and the male needs to inform the female, by means of the correct courtship behaviour, that he is a suitor and not her next meal. In the garden spider, *Araneus diadematus*, the male carries out a particular pattern of web shaking during courtship. However in the closely related *Argyope bruennichi* he is eaten by the female as soon as copulation has ended. The problem has been solved by *Pisaura mirabilis*, a spider which lives among leaves on low lying ground, and which does not make a web. The male spider catches a fly which he wraps up in silk. He presents this to the female, and while she is engaged in eating it, he can mate with her in comparative safety.

Many of the separate segments of behaviour found in the courtship pattern are ritualised forms of submissive or aggressive gestures. Sometimes juvenile behaviour patterns such as food begging are carried out as ritualised courtship patterns, in which one animal performs either mock or real feeding behaviour to the other. In higher primates, such as the baboon, juvenile feeding at the nipple is ritualised into the lip smacking movements which are used during sexual encounters, and kissing in man is thought to be a ritualised version of mouth-to-mouth feeding. Many other sections of human courtship behaviour are based on parental/juvenile relationships. The hand-in-hand walking, tender low pitched sounds made, caressing and embracing are all similar to actions made by parents to offspring. The adult human female, being on average smaller and more like the juvenile form than the male, elicits these tender parental gestures from him. The more 'baby-faced' and helpless the female appears, the more tender the male responses tend to be. In many human societies 'sex typing' of children still occurs from an early age; boys are allowed, or even encouraged, to express aggression towards other boys in their games, whereas girls are permitted to cry and seek help from their mothers. In the present Western feeling for sexual equality, sometimes too narrowly thought of as 'women's liberation', it is important that children should not learn to associate either protective dominance with maleness, or a dependent juvenile behaviour pattern with the female sex.

It is possible that some ritualised courtship patterns may enable the partner to assess the 'quality' of the future mate. Many animals make symbolic presents of nesting material during courtship, and this may show how efficient a nest builder or provider the animal will be.

A third important aspect of courtship behaviour is that it is genetically determined and species specific. This means that the pattern is the same for all the males, or all of the females, of a particular species and varies in some way in a different species. The difference may be an extremely small change in a specific movement which no longer acts as a releaser for the relevant behaviour in the prospective mate, or it may be an alteration in the timing mechanism so that synchronisation cannot occur. In this way wasteful matings between two closely related species, which would be infertile or would produce sterile offspring, can be avoided. The ten-spined stickleback, *Pungitius pungitius*, has a courtship pattern which is similar to that of the three-spined stickleback, but the male nuptial colours are different, being completely black in the ten-spined and red bellied in the three-spined. The colours appeal to the 'correct' females and so interbreeding does not occur.

Let us now consider some invertebrate and vertebrate courtship patterns.

In *Drosophila melanogaster* the female becomes receptive on the third day after emergence from the puparium and her receptivity reaches a peak at four and a half days, thereafter diminishing to the tenth day. During this period a male approaches the female and taps her body with his forefeet. He then moves around until he is facing her side, and makes complicated wing movements, first with both wings and then with only one. The air stream created by this rapid wing vibration mechanically stimulates the female's antennae. While this is going on he occasionally licks the female's abdomen, and if she is receptive he will mount her and she will open her genital plates. If he has not given the correct signals, or if she is not receptive, then she will kick him away. In watching such a display through a low power microscope, it is the visual signalling which impresses us. However courtship in *Drosophila* is as efficient in the dark as in the light and so it is likely that it is the mechanical stimulation produced by the wing movements that matters. Visual displays are recognised as such in some insects, such as the common glow worm, *Lampyris noctiluca*. The female is wingless and has to attract the winged male. This she does by producing light from her abdomen by means of the oxidation of a substance called luciferin by the enzyme luciferase. The male has large globular eyes well suited to find the glowing female.

Courtship in *Drosophila* is a fairly rapid process, although as we shall see in Chapter 22 there is a wide difference in the time taken by fast and slow maters. In the migratory locust, *Locusta migratoria*, the whole process of contact, mounting and copulation takes several hours. Although there is little in the way of specialised courtship behaviour, the male remains paired to the female (lying directly over her holding on with his first two pair of legs, and with his third pair of legs flexed) for a considerable time before genital contact is made. He remains on the female when she is laying her eggs in the sand, and as the female is most receptive to copulation just after ovipositing, an already mounted male will be able to mate with her. A male and female pair attracts other single males which try a 'take-over bid' – attacking from the side, or jumping onto the top of the already mounted male from in front or behind. So a column of three, or in some cases four, animals is made, the female at the base having to carry two or three males around. Direct take-overs by a male do not usually work, except when the female is actually egg laying. Then about one quarter of male attacks end with the

FIGURE 66 A

B

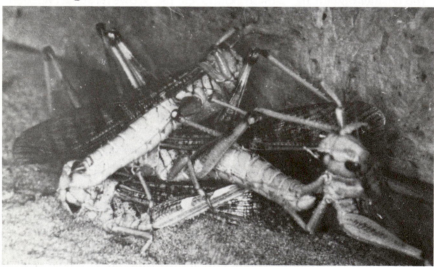

Courtship in the migratory locust.
A   Pairing.
The male is on top of the female, holding on to her by his first two pairs of legs.
B   A 'rough house' with locusts.
The female can be seen at the bottom left of the locusts. She is ovipositing, and her abdomen is buried in the sand.
The 'resident suitor' male is above her, holding on with two pairs of legs. His left back leg is kicking away a second male approaching from behind, and trying a 'take-over bid'. At the same time his right back leg is pushing away a third male which is trying to climb on from the front. The back legs of a fourth locust can be seen behind the combatants, suggesting that it is trying the side approach.

Photographs by courtesy of
G. R. G. Hayhurst

exchange of a new male for the passive, already mounted male. So courtship in the locust involves a series of aggressive encounters with other males. (Figure 66)

To turn now to vertebrates. The observations of the courtship behaviour of the great crested grebe, *Podiceps cristatus*, made in 1914 by Julian Huxley were of pioneering importance in the study of animal rituals. Grebes are phylogenetically rather primitive birds, but they have evolved some of the most elaborate courtship and pair bonding displays found anywhere in the vertebrates. Huxley's initial work was extended by Simmons in 1955, reassessed according to modern ethological theory by Huxley himself in 1966, and the dances have even been set to music by Walt Disney!

The great crested grebe is a distinctive bird of inland water with ear tufts and a neck frill in its summer plumage. At one time it was slaughtered for its satiny breast, called grebe 'fur' and was almost exterminated, but it is now increasing in number. It swims low in the water, often with its lower neck awash, and can swim particularly well under water. It flies little except during courtship when it makes frequent short flights.

Courtship begins in January, and a floating nesting platform of decaying water weed is made and anchored amongst reeds at the side of a lake. Eggs are laid sometime between April and August, and there are four eggs in a normal clutch. The female covers the eggs with nesting material whenever she leaves the nest, and both birds are involved in incubating the eggs and protecting the nestlings, carrying them around at first in a cradle formed by their slightly raised wings in a pick-a-back fashion. Both birds are noisy during courtship making repeated 'jik, jik' sounds, and the male also makes a loud, discordant 'gorrr'.

This brief summary gives no indication of the variety and elaborateness of the ceremonies involved, firstly in making and secondly in maintaining the pair bond between the male and female grebes.

The whole courtship pattern involves various movements, some of which are recognisable as ritualised aggression/appeasement gestures, and others as ritualised feeding or nest building activities. The sexes are outwardly almost identical, and most of the elements of the display are reciprocal, each bird performing the same movements.

The earliest ceremonies are ritual appeasement gestures. The two birds swim towards each other in an aggressive manner with raised crests and neck frills and then suddenly switch to the appeasement gesture of lowering the beak and shaking the head from side to side. This 'head shaking ceremony' is about five times more common than all the other ceremonies put together. (Figure 67–set 1 see next page)

Ritualised nest building activites are shown in the 'penguin dance'. In this the two birds dive and then emerge vertically from the water, lifting and touching each other, and presenting each other with mouthfuls of the same kind of water weed that is used to build the nest. (Figure 67 – set 2)

The 'cat position' may be adopted separately by both sexes, or the female may take this position, the male taking up what is known as the 'ghost position'. In this he dives and emerges slowly and vertically from the water in as thin a shape as possible. This display seems to combine elements of courtship and defence.

In the 'retreat ceremony' one bird involved in the 'head shaking ceremony' suddenly patters away across the water and then sinks into the 'cat position'. It rotates to face the other bird which has also entered the 'cat position'. The two birds may then link up again in another 'head shaking ceremony' from which a second 'retreat ceremony' may develop.

Each of these ceremonies is performed with maximum intensity when the mated birds come together after a period of separation, and they seem to reinforce the pair bonding. By pair bonding we mean the close and long lasting association between a male and a female which serves primarily for the cooperative rearing of the young.

FIGURE 67
Set 1

Courtship rituals in the great crested grebe.
A1, A2   The grebe in its unaroused, resting condition. The ear tufts and neck frill are flattened.
B1   Shows the bristled ear tufts and neck frill.
B2   View of the 'head shaking ceremony'.

FIGURE 67
Set 2

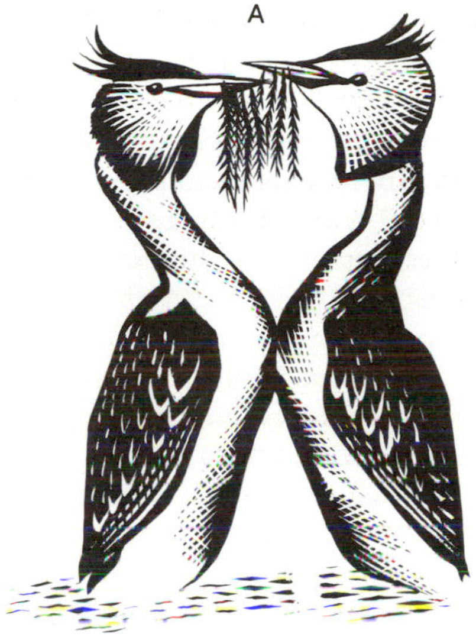

Courtship rituals in the great crested grebe, continued.
A   The 'penguin dance'.
The two birds arise from the water and present each other with pond weed. They may stay in this position for a few seconds.
B1   The 'cat position' which may be adopted by both sexes.
B2   The female grebe adopts the 'cat position'; the male has taken the 'ghost position'.
B3 and B4   Two views of the 'ghost position'.

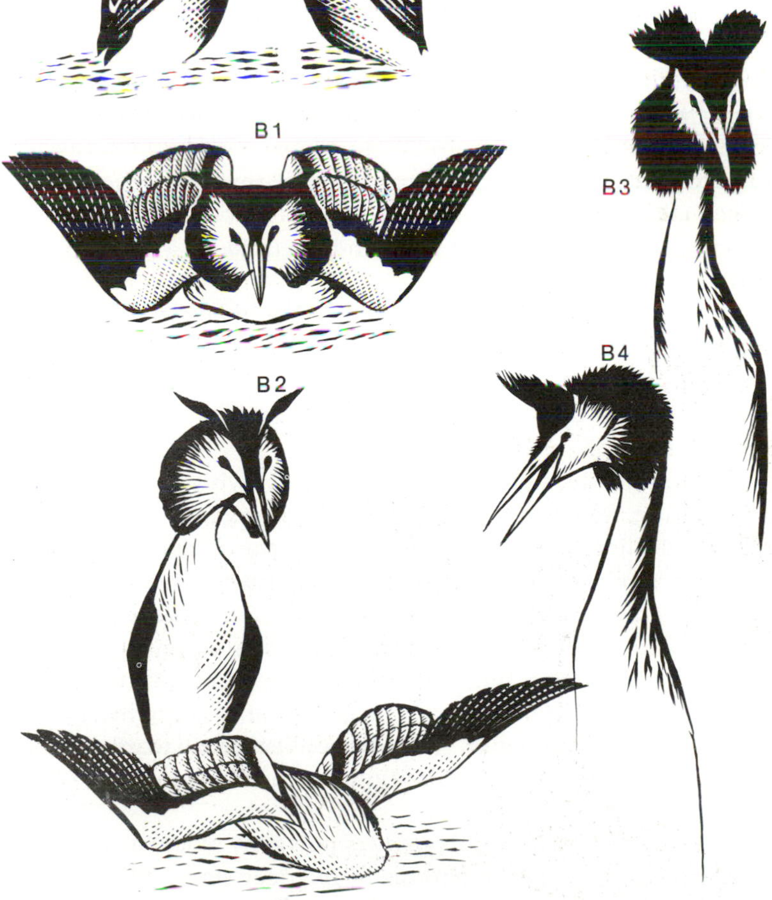

There are various strategies used in sexual reproduction. Pair bonding is found in monogamous species in which the male and the female stay together at least until a single brood is reared. Sometimes the pair bond may last a lifetime.

Monogamy is the result of various circumstances. It may occur if the territory contains such a scarce resource that two adults are required to protect it. It has been estimated that 91% of all birds are monogamous during the breeding season. Nesting sites may be difficult to acquire and so need constant defence.

Sometimes permanent pair bonding results as an adaptation to particularly difficult environments. The isopod crustacean, *Hemilepistus reaumuri*, lives in the dry steppes of Arabia and North Africa. Here it withdraws into burrows during the hottest, driest part of the year, and it has been found that each burrow is inhabited by an adult pair which remain mated for life.

Fairly permanent monogamy can also be advantageous in allowing an early start to breeding to be made. Coulson, in 1966, found that 64% adult female kittiwakes, *Rissa tridactyla*, retained their mate from the previous year. These females began to lay eggs three to seven days earlier, and reared a larger number of chicks than did other females which had taken a new mate. The already mated pairs did not need to expend energy in forming a pair bond and so could get a larger share of the available resources.

Orians has suggested that monogamy should be rare in mammals but common amongst birds. Because the female mammal produces the milk, there is little that the male parent can do in caring for the offspring, at least in its early life. However both male and female birds can collect food for, and feed their nestlings.

An alternative to monogamy is polygamy, which is any form of multiple mating. Sometimes a single female mates with many males as in the nuptial flight of the queen honey bee; this is called polyandry. This is relatively rare as the female usually makes much the larger parental investment in the offspring. In most animals the number of offspring to which a female can pass her genes is limited by the number of eggs she can produce, and the amount of parental care she must extend to the young. There is no advantage to her in being inseminated with sperm from various males. In the honey bee, brood rearing is taken over by the sterile workers, and this allows the queen to increase her egg laying.

A more usual pattern of polygamy is polygyny where a male mates with many females, as in the harems of red deer stags. The male can pass on his genes to a very large number of offspring by inseminating numerous females.

Polygyny tends to occur when a local or seasonal abundance of food allows a female to rear the offspring alone while the male goes off to find new mates. This, of course, is made easier if the young are precocial and can follow the mother to the feeding area, or to hiding places in order to escape from predators. Polygyny can occur among species with altricial young if they live in areas where there is a great variability of resources, such as occurs for birds which nest in marshes. In many polygynous species the males are long lived and can defer reproduction until they are well up the dominance ladder. What reproductive loss they incur by waiting is easily balanced by the increased number of females they can inseminate with their sperm when they become dominant.

In the next chapter we consider what may be the result of these different sexual arrangements, that is, family life.

18 Family life

One of the riddle questions which used to be asked was 'Which came first, the chicken or the egg?'. This was then altered to the idea that the chicken was only the egg's way of making another egg. More recently ethologists such as Richard Dawkins have elaborated the concept that both the chicken and the egg are only the gene's way of making more genes. Reproduction is therefore the way in which genes can 'ensure' that they will be passed on to the next generation. This being so, there are two basic patterns of reproduction. Asexual reproduction guarantees the passage of identical patterns of genes to the next generation, apart from mutation, but such a pattern might be completely destroyed by a change in the environment. Sexual reproduction gives variety; new combinations of genes are produced which possibly could be better than the original combination.

Whichever type of reproduction occurs, however, it is implicit in the scheme that enough offspring will survive to reach adulthood and their own reproduction to maintain the 'immortality' of the genes. Such survival may result either from a very large reproductive capacity and little or no parental care, or from a very small reproductive capacity and considerable parental care. Both systems are found in the vertebrates.

Cartilaginous fish are generally viviparous, or deposit single, well developed eggs in separate egg cases, as in the dogfish, whereas many bony fish, like the herring, dump the ova and sperm in millions, most of the offspring dying very early. Some bony fish, however, show elaborate parental care. As we have seen, the male stickleback protects the young fish. The female *Tilapia*, one of the mouth breeding cichlids, keeps the young for about ten days within her mouth. During the following few days they are allowed to swim out on their own, but they rapidly return to her mouth if threatened.

Amphibians usually have a slightly reduced reproductive capacity, but this is offset by the fact that they have a mating process. Amphibians generally show no parental care, although the male midwife toad, *Alytes obstetricans*, winds strings of from twenty to a hundred fertilised eggs around his back legs and carries them about until the tadpoles have hatched. (Figure 68)

Reptiles are very variable. Some, like crocodiles, build nests of mud in which the eggs are laid. When the young hatch they make sounds which are heard by the mother and she breaks open the nest to release

FIGURE 68

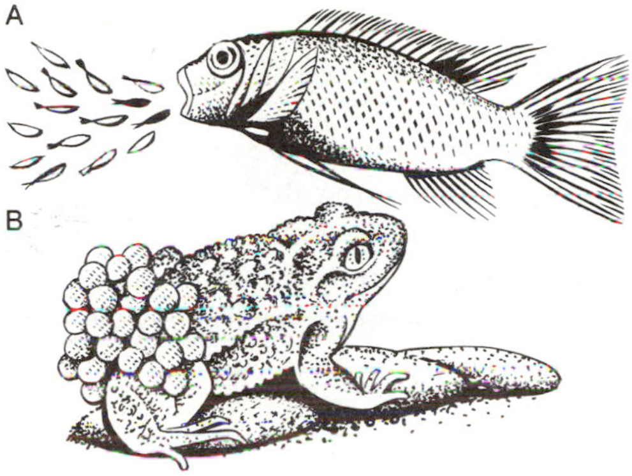

Two examples of parental care in lower vertebrates.
A   Young *Tilapia* swimming back to their mother. She keeps the young fish within her mouth until they are ten days old. For the next few days they are allowed to swim outside her mouth, but return if in danger. They swim towards dark regions; some of them try to enter the gill openings or the eyes of the mother.
B   The male midwife toad carrying around strings of eggs.

them. She carries them about in her mouth, and generally invests a lot of energy in caring for them. Turtles, on the other hand, leave their clutches of eggs buried in the sand on beaches, and there is great mortality in the newly hatched young as they struggle to make their way down to the water.

The great peaks of parental care are found in the birds and the mammals, both of which are warm blooded. Precocial offspring are born with their temperature regulating devices already functional and so the type of care they need differs from that needed by altricial offspring which are usually born featherless or hairless.

Parental care in these two classes of animals may consist of complicated behaviour patterns both before and after the birth of the offspring.

Before the birth there is often a change in the behaviour shown to other adults; the female may become more intolerant of them if she is to give birth in seclusion. Both birds and mammals which have altricial young will build nests, although sometimes mammals will take over and adapt existing burrows. Both polecats and foxes will make lairs in rabbit burrows, often by killing the original occupants; the common shrew inhabits vole, mole or mice burrows.

Nest building in a female bird is stimulated by increased oestrogen production, which also brings about the development of a defeathered and highly vascularised area on her breast. This naked brood patch is very sensitive to the feel of the nest, and this influences the bird in her choice of nest material, and also stimulates her to lay her eggs. The eggs are then incubated, the mother placing them against her brood patch, and so they are kept almost as warm as she is herself. Sometimes all the incubating is carried out by the male parent. The male Emperor penguin supports the single egg on the top surface of his feet, (thereby insulating it from the icy ground) for two months and during this time he may lose up to one third of his body weight.

As we have mentioned in Chapter 8 the calls made by bird embryos have an effect on the parents which are incubating them. The sounds alter the parental pattern of rising and settling, but also have more important effects. Impekoven found that each one of thirty-one laughing gull females which had been sitting on a pipping, vocal egg accepted a strange chick immediately at the right hatching time, but fifteen out of twenty-six birds which had been incubating earlier, non-vocal embryos reacted aggressively by pecking at the strange chick.

So incubation is not only for the direct well-being of the embryonic bird; it also primes the parental responses of the female when the chicks hatch.

Some mammals also prepare for parturition by building a nest, and as we have seen in Chapter 4, this may be under the control of fluctuating reproductive hormones in the pregnant animal. Gestation and parturition seem to favour a very rapid establishment of maternal behaviour. On giving birth mice, rat and hamster females immediately start to lick the new-born offspring and Noirot found that the 'priming' of maternal responses in these small mammals seems to occur in a possibly similar way to that found by Impekoven in the laughing gull. A live mouse pup was enclosed in a perforated metal box and presented to adult female mice for short periods. Their behaviour when later they were presented with strange pups was compared with that of control females which had not had sniffing contact with the mouse pup. The treated females immediately carried out maternal behaviour; the untreated control animals showed exploratory and avoidance behaviour.

When the young birds or mammals have been born, it is necessary that they should be fed.

Young birds may be nidicolous – that is they remain in the nest, or nidifugous if they quickly leave the nest. All altricial birds are nidicolous, but precocial birds may be either nidicolous or nidifugous. Sea birds which live on narrow ledges cannot follow their parents, even if they are physically capable of moving around. All nidicolous birds must be fed by one or other parent, and the techniques used vary from species to species. Sometimes the parent bird arrives back at the nest with a beakful of insects, and sometimes the food is swallowed by the parent and regurgitated for the young. Large birds of prey carry the food back in their talons, and the strength needed for an eagle to carry a young antelope in this way is considerable. Whatever method is used, the food then has to be passed from the adult to the young birds. In many birds the dark shape of the parent or the shaking of the nest as the parent lands on it, acts as a releaser for the gape response in the young bird, and this in turn acts as a releaser for feeding behaviour in the adult. This has been utilised by the cuckoo in its social parasitism. The cuckoo egg hatches earlier than those of the true mother bird, and the young cuckoo proceeds to gape intensely at the parents, thereby inducing them to feed it. The young cuckoo edges the other eggs out of the nest, and if nestlings are present it will push them over the nest rim. If the nestlings stay on the nest rim they quickly cool down, weaken and do not have the energy to gape, and so they are ignored by the parent birds and die.

Although the female mammal needs to obtain food for herself, she does not have to carry it back for her new-born young. The pattern of suckling varies in different species; new-born laboratory rats may be almost continually on the mother's nipples, whereas young rabbits tend to have large meals of milk at twenty-four hour intervals.

In nesting animals it is also necessary for the mother to attend to nest sanitation. The old proverb about animals not fouling their own nests has its basis in fact. Adult blackbirds will, after feeding their offspring, tap the nestlings until they shuffle their tail ends over the nest rim, the excretory products therefore falling outside the nest. Some birds collect excretory pellets and remove them. The general licking and cleaning of the young, particularly of the ano-genital area, carried out by some mammal mothers has the effect of making the young urinate. It has been found that without such stimulation the young will die from a general disturbance of their water balance in the absence of urination even though they are well fed and kept warm. If ever you are hand rearing baby rats you will need to use a piece of wet, warm cotton wool to ensure that this does not happen.

Because young birds and mammals have a high surface area to volume ratio, it is important that they are surrounded by insulating material to cut their heat losses. Semi-closed nests are an advantage, and breeding burrows can reach high temperatures.

Any situation which seems likely to remove one of the young from the nest will be met with aggression on the part of the mother. In experiments with deermice, *Perimyscus maniculatus*, in which the investigator tried to remove a pup from the nest, King found that the extremely aggressive attack response by the mother diminished as the litter neared weaning age.

If the young accidentally stray out of the nest they are likely to die from cold or predation unless the mother can retrieve them. Rodents, lagomorphs and carnivores carry their young back to the nest by the scruff of the neck. Often retrieval is stimulated by sound signals between the mother and the wandering offspring, this occurs frequently in birds which breed in dense colonies. Very young rodents emit ultrasonic vibrations which can be heard by the mother, but scent becomes more important after a time. In the gerbil the mother rubs her ventral scent gland over the pups, and so they all are recognisable to her.

However, even if parental care is excellent, and the nest well hidden and guarded, a situation may arise in which a predator must be attracted away from the nest position. Different species have evolved different distraction displays. One of the commonest is injury feigning on the part of the parent. The female may leave the nest, and, after flying conspicuously low, will flop down just in front of the predator. Black throated divers, *Gavia arctica*, spread one wing as if it is broken and then paddle around in circles. Sometimes the predator is distracted by special display flights of the adult; this occurs in oyster catchers, *Haematopus ostralegus*. Other birds lead the predator away from the nest by squatting, as if brooding, on another piece of ground.

As we can see, for birds and mammals being a parent involves a large repertoire of different behaviour patterns: nest building; incubation; feeding; nest sanitation; retrieval; defence; all need to be efficiently carried out while the offspring are small. Even after the young have passed the most vulnerable stage and can feed themselves, it is possible that the adults have to carry out an extended training period to equip the offspring for social living.

Poirier has suggested that primate social development passes through four stages. At first the young primate is helpless, and its only social relationship is that of holding onto its mother, and drinking her milk. As it gets older it reaches a transition stage in which, although the relationship with its mother is still very important, it can leave her for increasingly long periods. During these first two stages touch is particularly important. As Harlow showed with young rhesus monkeys, the tactile stimulus given by the 'cloth mother' was necessary to reassure the young and to enable them to explore new and frightening objects. Gradually the young primate's peers become more important to it than its mother, and during this time there is a corresponding reduction in juvenile behaviour patterns. Finally these juvenile patterns disappear, unless they become ritualised as courtship movements, and adult behaviour takes over. Such a progression can be seen with human children with the gradual development of independence and the importance of peer groups at particular ages. To little boys, the 'gang' matters, with its complicated rules and dominance hierarchy.

One of the most important aspects of higher vertebrate social development is the use of play. Although it places the participants in a vulnerable position because of the danger of unnoticed predators, or even the aggressive response of adults of the same social group, it increases their fitness at a later stage. Play with sticks, leaves and grass stems seems to give young chimpanzees more opportunity to develop insightful solutions to problems which they later meet. It is also a very useful socialising process. In 539 chimpanzee play sessions observed by Jane van Lawick-Goodall 75% involved pairs of animals, 19% were trios and 4% were made up of four or more animals. Chimpanzees play most between the ages of two and four, and, although they retain a close relationship with the mother for up to six years, their behaviour after weaning at about four years old becomes less juvenile and more adolescent. In carnivores play fights are used not just for training the young in the necessary fighting techniques but also to hammer out a dominance order.

A break in the relationship between the mother and the offspring occurs at weaning. As we have already mentioned, maternal aggression towards the infant builds up at this stage. The female macaque, *Macaca mulatta*, removes the infant's lips from her nipple by forcibly pushing the young animal away and placing it on the ground. The infant screams in protest and tries to get back into a clinging position. A yearling moose is driven away by its mother when she has a new calf and spends the next few months lingering around trying to get back to her. When the rut starts in the autumn the young moose has a brief chance to get near its mother again. However if it is female it is treated by her as a rival, and if it is male it is driven away by the dominant male. This is the final break; the young animal now really starts to become independent.

It has been thought that weaning aggression is a mechanism whereby the female can force the young to become independent, irrespective of any further litters she may have. Trivers sees it as a result of natural selection working in opposite ways in the two generations. A time is reached when it becomes more profitable to the mother to pass on her genes to a second offspring or litter, rather than to continue to invest in an offspring which already has a good chance of survival. However from the infant's point of view, its fitness depends on it gaining as long a period of parental care as it can. Hence the parent/offspring conflict.

We are therefore back to the idea with which we started this chapter. All the complicated strategies and ploys carried out during reproduction and family care add up to the way in which genes 'ensure' that as many copies of themselves as possible will be made.

19 Migration

Many animals make large scale movements during their lifetime. In those with a relatively long life a double movement, 'there and back again' is possible; in short lived species a single movement may be all that can be carried out, with a possible return journey in the next generation. Any such movement which takes an animal, or a group of animals, away from its original habitat can be called a migration, and although many migrators are well known and obvious, there are many other cases in which the details are just beginning to be understood.

Migrations, like other instinctive patterns, are phenomena which have been regarded in the past as mysterious miracles. Seasonal birds turn up in an area, not just on the expected day, but also at the usual nesting sites. The white stork returns in April to the high nesting platforms placed on house roofs in Europe after its winter stay in Africa. Both turtles and salmon return to their own birth places in order to lay eggs; the salmon somehow finds the same river, and the turtle climbs out on to the same beach. Eels leave their fresh water surroundings and all make their way across the Atlantic Ocean to the Sargasso Sea, where they mate, the young eels returning in swarms to European rivers again. Whales move to warmer waters to breed, and return to the Antarctic to feed and grow. Land mammals such as caribou move south to spend the winter in Mid-western Canada, returning north as the spring arrives. Lemmings make one way migrations from the original population when the population pressure increases. Bats which have been tagged in the southern parts of the United States have been recaptured eight hundred miles away. Many invertebrates are also known to migrate. One of the best known insect migrators is the monarch butterfly which moves from Canada to overwinter in the southern parts of the United States. The locust has been around since our ancestors first started to grow grain for themselves and their animals, and was one of the biblical plagues of Egypt. The large white butterfly, although it is a permanent resident of Britain, is reinforced by immigration every year. Molluscs, such as the squid, move over one hundred miles along the coastline of Europe, and many crustaceans migrate vertically every twenty-four hours from the depths to the surface of the oceans.

Given, then, that large migratory movements occur in many different groups of animals, one would expect that the 'reasons' for migration would be varied.

Migration is a hazardous affair; many of the animals which set out do not complete the journey. Crosswinds which keep land birds over the sea where they cannot feed or settle cause much mortality. Navigational errors in bad weather also add to the death toll. Even for those animals which are successful there is the cost of using up body fat reserves. Sometimes the climatic conditions in the arrival area are temporarily severe with a consequent reduction in the food available for the hungry travellers, and an insectivorous bird which makes a slight mistake in timing can arrive before the insects which make up its food have hatched, or emerged from their puparia.

With all of these problems to be overcome it would seem likely that migration would be exceptional rather than common, but this is not what is found. There must be advantages for those animals which actually achieve their 'goal' which permit them to breed more efficiently, and so increase the frequency of their genes within the population.

Let us consider some of the possible advantages and see how they apply to particular groups of migrants.

First of all, migration *could* be a way of avoiding the harsher extremes of temperature. Birds, for example, could leave Britain or other northern countries in autumn, at the beginning of the cold season, and could travel to tropical and subtropical regions. It is the sort of journey which sounds reasonable. Think how many people would like to follow the example of the swallow and get away to warmer climates and avoid the British winter. An avoidance of harsh temperatures is found in some animals, such as the Blue Whale which leaves its Antarctic feeding grounds to breed in warmer waters during the southern winter. The Blue Whale lives almost exclusively on a planktonic crustacean, *Euphausia superba*, known as krill, which is present in enormous numbers in cold Antarctic waters. The euphausians are the primary consumers in that particular food web feeding on diatoms, most of which have a definite fat content. The euphausians also contain carotene and vitamin A in their eyes, and this finds its way to the whale's liver and blubber. The distribution of krill varies inversely with the temperature of the water. Cold water contains more carbon dioxide and oxygen than warm water, and this allows the food web to flourish. Large currents occur around the edges of the pack ice, and these stir up and distribute mineral salts. However the low temperature of the water makes it hazardous for the new-born whale, and birth takes place in warmer waters. So we see that the whale moves away from its usual feeding grounds to breed.

The whale, like other aquatic animals, is in an environment in which temperature tends to vary fairly regularly and to a relatively small extent, both with season and with latitude. Climatic conditions are much more variable for land animals. European birds, for example, may be subjected to extremely hot, or cold wet summers, and so it would not be efficient for them to begin migratory journeys purely as a result of falling temperature. Some other environmental factor must be important for land animals. Most birds are active only by day, and so an increased daylength could enable them to obtain more food for their nestlings.

There is evidence from two studies on the Eastern robin of the United States that increased daylength does indeed enable parent birds to gather more food. One study was of a robin family in Alaska where the sun stayed above the horizon throughout the day and night, and the other was of a robin family in Ohio. The Ohio nestlings were fed by their parents every ten minutes throughout a sixteen hour day, and were ready to leave the nest at thirteen days old. The Alaska family were fed at ten minute intervals throughout a twenty-one hour day, and were ready to fly away from the nest at nine days old. The parental effort involved in making over one hundred and twenty feeding visits each day is enormous.

So we have a second migratory advantage; longer days allow some parents to collect more food for their offspring.

A further advantage to a territorial species is that there is a large, temporarily unclaimed area available in which to establish nesting territories. The efficient, early arrivals can thus rear their young with less difficulty.

It is sometimes easier to see the value of 'one way' migrations, in which a section of an established population moves away to start a new population elsewhere. A diminishing food supply is often the trigger for movement, but in many migratory insects it occurs as soon as the adult emerges. As many adults emerge at approximately the same time, large migratory groups are formed which are very obvious. This emergence migration is a useful adaptation which ensures dispersal and the colonisation of new areas, and prevents overcrowding of the original population.

Emigration in rodent populations seems to have the same effect of preventing overcrowding of the original population. Various workers have studied population cycles and emigration in small rodents, and it is now thought that in the field vole, *Microtus agrestis*, populations comprise two broad classes of genotypes with different behaviour patterns. (The genotype analysis was not carried out from behaviour patterns, but from electrophoretic analysis of blood proteins). One class has superior reproductive capacity but is intolerant of a high population density; the other class has adapted to survival under crowded conditions by being aggressive, but its reproduction rate is lower. When the population increases, the density intolerant animals leave and the aggressive stay behind. This, of course, reduces the population size, both because of the emigration and because of the reduced reproduction rate of the animals left behind. When the population reaches a lower level, then the remaining density intolerant but highly reproductive animals again start to increase. So the characteristic population cycles with their associated migrations occur.

It is likely that a similar high population intolerance occurs in lemmings, and this would account for the periodic migrations which have entered into the folk tales of many peoples. These apocryphal tales suggest that periodically lemming armies march, or run, out of the northern regions behind a leader lemming, eating crops and biting people in their path, until eventually they all follow the leader as he swims out to sea, not a single animal surviving. In fact the emigration is unorganised; there is no army and no leader. Individual animals behave similarly at the same time, and so the emigration looks like a socially organised gathering. Lemmings being nocturnal, the migrating animals travel by night and mortality from many causes is very great. Losses are high, but the migration cannot be thought of as mass suicide.

As we mentioned earlier, it is vitally important that the timing of migration is right, but how does a swallow in southern Africa know when to start a journey which will finish, at just the right time, in Britain? It is easier to see what makes it leave Britain to go back to Africa in late summer, for here reduced daylength could clearly be important. In his pioneering work on the physiology of migration, William Rowan artificially altered the daylength to which birds were exposed, and found that increasing daylength was correlated with an enlargement of the ovaries or testes. Kramer, in the late 1940s, placed songbirds in circular cages during the migratory period and found that they spontaneously oriented in a particular direction. Emlen, working with the North American indigo bunting *Passerina cyanea*, was able to draw conclusions about the physiological state of migratory buntings and also about their method of navigation, and we return to this latter topic in the next chapter. The indigo bunting breeds throughout the eastern United States and migrates, nocturnally, in autumn to overwinter in the Bahamas and central America. Two groups of buntings were taken. The birds in the control group were kept in a room where they could fly around and where the daylength was similar to that in central America. The males in this group moulted and developed pre-nuptial plumage between February and early April, as they would have done if they really had been in central America at that time. They also built up large subcutaneous fat reserves and began to get restless at night in April and May – a time when they would normally be ready to fly back to the eastern United States for the summer.

The experimental birds were subjected to the normal daylength for central America until December, but then exposed to spring daylengths of fifteen hours. This induced the development of pre-nuptial plumage in January. From the beginning of March the daylength was progressively shortened to simulate a premature autumn, and the birds moulted out of their breeding plumage. They did, however, build up fat reserves, which in the normal situation would have enabled them to fly south to central America in the autumn.

There are still many aspects of migration which we do not understand. As we have seen, it is sometimes possible to link up the physiological change which leads to migration with an external cue such as altered daylength, or to understand migration connected with population cycles through the genetic constitution of the organisms involved. Obviously, in a migratory species, the efficient animals are those which actually survive the journey and so have the resultant advantages in rearing their offspring, and so efficient migration will be selected for. But some migratory movements seem, to us, to give few advantages to be paid for by enormous energy expenditure and greatly increased vulnerability. One of the most famous migrators is the Arctic tern which regularly travels from arctic to antarctic regions. There are many recorded taggings and recoveries; a tern was recovered in Natal, South Africa, only one hundred and sixteen days after it had been ringed in Labrador as a downy chick. Another bird was recovered on October 30th of one year, in South Africa, which had been ringed in Greenland on July 8th. A bird ringed in Murmansk on the arctic shores of the USSR was recovered in Western Australia. So these birds regularly fly over eight thousand miles to make a migratory journey, followed a few months later by a similar return trip. (Figure 69)

In this chapter we have been considering some of the possible advantages to be gained from migration, and also some of the physiological changes which occur, but obviously one of the most important aspects is that the animal can navigate well enough to reach its destination. How it does this, we consider next.

FIGURE 69

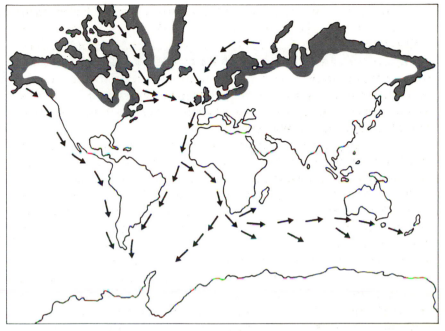

The autumn migration of the Arctic tern.
The shaded northern zones are the breeding
grounds.
Arrows show the general direction of the autumn
migration, which begins in July and continues to
October.
The return flight occurs in the spring.

Based on Dorst.

20 Homing and navigation

Homing is, in a superficial way, the opposite of migration. In homing, an animal which has been displaced in some way finds its way back to its home site, whereas in migration the animal leaves its home site. The orientation required for homing is different from a migratory orientation, as the necessary path depends upon the particular displacement. Displacement experiments subject the animal to purely artificial situations but it is possible that the homing ability they demonstrate has evolved as a method of counteracting displacement produced by abnormally strong winds.

Most homing experiments have used birds, and one of the best known homers is the pigeon. Pigeons have been used as message carriers for many centuries and, now that this has been superseded by radio transmission, they provide sport for large numbers of enthusiasts. The pigeons are reared in a loft which they can enter or leave through a swinging door, and they begin to make local flights as soon as they are able. Systematic training begins when a bird is three to six months old; it is taken in a closed basket to a place some distance from the loft, and is then released. Some birds do not return to the loft, but those which do become increasingly adept at homing. The training distances are gradually increased, and some young birds can successfully learn to find their way home over one hundred miles in their first season.

Although the pigeon is the homing animal which first springs to mind its feats are easily outshone by those of the Manx shearwater, *Puffinus puffinus*. These birds breed in burrows on islands around the north and west coasts of Britain, except curiously enough the Isle of Man from where they get their name. Some birds taken from the island of Skokholm off southwest Wales were released at various places in England and returned to their breeding burrows. Other birds were taken to Venice and returned after fourteen days. Considering that Manx shearwaters do not fly over land, it is likely that these birds flew over the Mediterranean, through the Straits of Gibraltar, and then up over the eastern Atlantic to get back to Skokholm, and they must have averaged two hundred and sixty-five miles a day over the fourteen days. A similarly spectacular homing flight occurred when two Manx shearwaters were taken by air to Boston, Massachusetts, USA and then released. One of them did not return, but the other was back in its nest within twelve and a half days.

Even these exceptional flights are smaller than those made by albatrosses, taken from their nests in the Midway Islands in the Pacific Ocean, and transported by air to various distant points. Out of eighteen birds removed in this way, fourteen returned to their nests, the longest journey being of four thousand, one hundred and twenty miles in thirty-two days.

So it is clear that many birds have this ability to find their way home, particularly at the breeding season when such homing may be vitally necessary for the welfare of the nestlings.

Many different studies have been carried out to try to understand how the bird manages to fly in the right direction from a place it has never seen before and which therefore has no landmarks it can recognise, when it has a total lack of 'knowledge' of everything between this place and its home. In some investigations the birds have been carefully watched from helicopters from the moment of release until they return to their nests, but although this can give information about the path taken, it does not tell us what cues the bird uses to find the correct direction. Many birds can head in the right direction almost from the moment of release, irrespective of the position of the cage opening, and this was shown in a series of experiments by Matthews with pigeons and Manx shearwaters.

The initial heading is one aspect of either a homing or a migration flight which can be investigated in the laboratory. Kramer, in the 1940s carried out experiments with starlings which had been hand reared from an early age and so were very tame and used to being caged. A starling was placed in a circular cage suspended within an outer container. (Figure 70)

The observer lay on his back on the floor and watched the movements of the bird through the transparent floor of the apparatus. The walls of the outer container could be altered in various ways. In some experiments they were made opaque so that the bird could not see the horizon, but could see the sky through the clear top. In other experiments the top of the apparatus was opaque, but windows were left in the walls. In this apparatus one starling flew backwards and forwards from the centre perch to the northwest of the cage if the experiment was performed in the spring; an orientation which corresponded with the normal migratory direction of starlings in the area where it had been taken, as a very young bird, from its original nest. However if mirrors were placed by the wall windows in such a way that the apparent position of the sun was rotated through ninety degrees, then the starling flew to the southwest. Such a result suggested that the sun was an important environmental cue, and this was reinforced by the fact that the headings became random when sky was overcast.

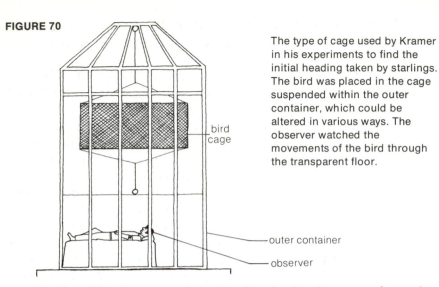

FIGURE 70

The type of cage used by Kramer in his experiments to find the initial heading taken by starlings. The bird was placed in the cage suspended within the outer container, which could be altered in various ways. The observer watched the movements of the bird through the transparent floor.

bird cage

outer container

observer

In the 1950s Sauer was investigating the development of song in the European warbler, and it was necessary to rear young birds in complete isolation to see if they performed the species-specific song at the right age. Franz Sauer and his wife became expert foster parents and managed to rear the birds to healthy, breeding, migratory adults. As well as their main study on the song, they tried their warblers, which are nocturnal migrants, in a circular cage similar to that used by Kramer a few years before, but exposed them not only to the natural night sky, but also to the 'night sky' in a planetarium. Planetarium work eliminates the difficulty of wet, overcast nights which affect both the birds and the bird watchers, and also makes it possible apparently to change the seasons at will. A further important aspect of the Sauers' work was that their experimental birds had been reared in complete isolation, and had not, until the experiment, ever seen the sky.

The results showed that some of these warblers consistently headed in the direction which corresponded to their normal migratory flight. This direction depended on the physiological condition of the birds; in the spring when the birds were coming into their breeding condition the headings were to the north, whereas in the autumn the birds headed south. If, by means of hormone injections, the birds were brought to breeding condition at the wrong season, then they headed north as though it were spring. It became obvious that these birds were using the position of the stars to give them a heading direction, and in certain cases were able to do this on their first exposure to the night sky. Some built-in genetic mechanism which enabled the brain to respond to particular visual patterns which had not been seen before was postulated.

Emlen repeated these experiments with North American indigo buntings, but devised an apparatus which was self recording. (Figure 71)

When the birds began to show nocturnal activity in April/May or September/October, they were placed individually in cone-shaped cages lined with white blotting paper and with an ink pad in the base. The bird could see the sky, and it jumped up the cone at frequent intervals, leaving inky footprints on the blotting paper. The next morning the blotting paper, with its inky record of the bird's nocturnal activity could be scrutinised. On clear nights in spring the birds jumped to the north east; in September/October they jumped to the south west. The apparatus was then taken into the planetarium, and the birds' orientation noted, and it was found that if the 'sky' was rotated to be three, six or twelve hours ahead or behind normal time the birds maintained the correct position with the stars, and so did not seem to use an internal clock which measured the passage of time. By shutting off various sections of the 'sky' it was possible to find the particular star 'markers' to which the birds responded. Emlen found that young birds were not as good at finding the correct heading as adults, and birds with no visual experience of the night sky produced randomly scattered jumps. However after the young birds had spent the equivalent of a few nights in the planetarium, they began to take the right direction.

So both the sun and the stars can be used to give the correct initial heading for a bird. However, after setting off on a homing flight or a migratory journey, the bird must maintain the correct position in relation to the sun or star marker used. This maintenance of the correct orientation is brought about by various means in different animals. Insects, with their compound eyes can keep certain ommatidia stimulated, but it is not yet clear how the process occurs in vertebrates. Hoffmann's experiments with starlings, which we have described in Chapter 6, showing the connection of an internal clock with a sun compass, have been repeated with pigeons, with very similar results.

FIGURE 71

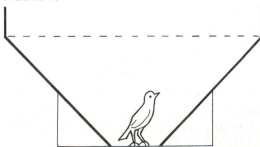

Emlen's experiments with North American Indigo Buntings. The bird stands on an ink pad at the base of a blotting paper cone, and can see the sky through the mesh top.
Periodically it jumps up onto the cone, leaving a record in the form of inky footprints.

Birds seem to amalgamate information they receive from their sun or star compass with other information from their surroundings. Starlings which normally migrate from eastern Europe to northern France were netted and ringed in Holland and then taken to Switzerland where they were released. Adult birds which had made a similar migratory flight the previous year compensated for the displacement and arrived at their correct destination, whereas the young, naive birds flew on the correct compass line and arrived in Spain. (Figure 72) So other environmental cues as well as the compass must be used. Certainly for short flights animals depend on already learned visual patterns around their destination. Solitary wasps find their way back to the nest primarily by a sun compass, but secondarily by the recognition of the nest in relation to other objects. If, while the wasp is inside, the nest is encircled with small objects such as pine cones, then the wasp learns the total visual pattern when it emerges. If the pine cones are then moved from the nest area while the wasp is away, and are rearranged somewhere nearby, then the wasp will fly to the pine cone ring, and not to its nest. (Figure 73)

FIGURE 72

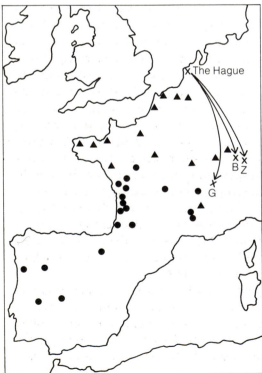

Experiments on the orientation of starlings carried out by Perdeck.
Migratory starlings were netted at the Hague and taken to Switzerland, where they were released at Basel, Geneva and Zurich.
Recoveries showed that young birds continued to fly south-west but most adult birds flew to their normal wintering areas.

▲ – adult birds
● – juvenile birds
B – Basel
G – Geneva
Z – Zurich

FIGURE 73

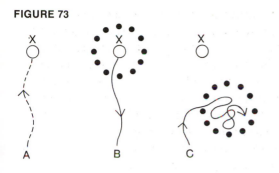

Homing in the wasp.
A   The wasp flies to the nest, X.
B   The nest is encircled with fir cones while the wasp is within. When the wasp flies away it remembers the pattern of fir cones.
C   The fir cones have been displaced and the wasp, on returning, searches within the ring for the nest.

So far we have been considering those visual cues which man would also be able to use. We certainly can orient by means of recognised landmarks, or by the position of the sun or of the stars. However there is one visual aspect for which we are poorly equipped, that is the reception of polarised light. The light emitted by the sun vibrates in all planes, and so is unpolarised, but it becomes polarised on travelling through the earth's atmosphere. The pattern of polarisation can be used for navigation by animals such as bees even if the sun is not visible.

It is obvious therefore that many types of visual cues are used for navigation, but it has been found by Schmidt-Koenig that 60% of pigeons released wearing frosted contact lenses can find their way home. So their navigational system must have non-visual components.

European robins were investigated at the University of Frankfurt, and it was found that they could take the right heading for a spring migratory flight even if they could see neither the sun nor the stars. If, however, the cage was placed in a magnetic field opposite to the normal, then the birds changed their heading accordingly. As the earth's magnetic field is not generally parallel to the earth's surface (a compass needle dips at one end if it is freely suspended in the vertical as well as in the horizontal plane), one would expect the bird to react to this declination rather than to a change in the horizontal field, and this is what the investigators found. A changed horizontal field had less effect on the robin than a changed tilted field. So it looks as if the birds do have a magnetic compass. Other experiments have been carried out in which birds have been subjected to altered magnetic fields.

Keeton attached bar magnets to the backs of one group of pigeons, and brass bars of equal mass to pigeons in a control group. The pigeons were released about twenty miles from their home loft in sunny conditions and all returned quickly and safely. However in overcast conditions the 'brass birds' returned normally, but the 'magnet birds' were disoriented.

Walcott carried out similar experiments but used small Helmholtz coils, one on the top of the pigeon's head and another round its neck like a collar. Each bird also carried a battery pack to power the coils, and also an attached radio transmitter which allowed the bird to be tracked. The polarity of the magnetic field surrounding the bird could be altered by changing the current flow. The pigeon had no difficulty in flying in the right direction under cloudy skies if the artificially produced North pointed downwards; if it pointed upwards then the bird flew away from home.

It is now thought that homing pigeons use many navigational devices. Both sun compasses and magnetic compasses have been shown to give good navigation. Used together they produce the great accuracy which is the basis of the sport of pigeon racing.

A more straightforward, and to man a more understandable, method of navigation is by the detection of chemicals. As we have already seen, male moths may travel long distances attracted by a few molecules of a pheromone produced by the female, and such well developed chemical sensory systems are found in many animals. Green turtles travel from the coast of Brazil to Ascension Island to lay their eggs, and it is possible that chemical cues from the island are carried in the prevailing westward current. Different chemical cues are thought to direct the turtles up or down the Brazilian coast until they reach the correct latitude. Once they have established this, they navigate with a sun compass as well.

Hasler, in 1951, showed that fish have the ability to detect small concentrations of chemicals in different natural fresh waters, and he suggested that the salmon, *Salmo salar*, becomes conditioned to the smell of its birthplace during the time it lives in the river before setting out to the sea. So when the fish have navigated, by some as yet unknown means, to the correct coastline, they then find the correct river mouth by scent.

A great amount of work is going on at present to discover the details of how animals manage to navigate as efficiently as some of them do. In the past accurate tracking of the animals depended on tagging and recovery, but this is rather a 'hit and miss' affair. Now more sophisticated techniques are available. Migrating birds can be tracked by radar, and flocks of birds are now known to cause the patterns called radar angels which were such a nuisance to the radar scanners of World War 2 and afterwards. Individual migrants can be followed by attached radio transmitters and this has been used for tracking larger animals such as mammals. There is still a long way to go, however, before all the secrets of navigation will have been discovered.

21 Interspecific relationships

So far we have been mainly considering the behaviour patterns shown by an animal to its conspecifics, that is to other animals of the same species. However animals do not live isolated from other species. A community in a particular habitat is a complex assembly of different species, all of which interact to some extent, if only with aggressive, predatorial behaviour or defensive, prey behaviour. Some species have evolved much more complicated inter-relationships, which may be temporary or permanent.

Biologists differ in the terms they use to describe these relationships. Some describe any relationship between two different species as symbiosis, which, literally means living together. Others restrict the term to a relationship in which both the partners benefit. There are three categories of interspecific relationships, which vary according to the benefits or harm accrued by the participants.

1 Mutualism, or symbiosis in its restricted use.
Here both organisms benefit in some way from the association. It may be such a permanent and fixed relationship that the two organisms can almost be thought of as one, as in the case of the green alga and the fungus which together make up the plant body of a lichen, or the two organisms may retain their integrity and use each other in particular circumstances.

2 Commensalism.
In this, one organism benefits and, as far as we can see, the other is not affected in any way. It is sometimes very difficult to judge whether a relationship shows commensalism, or whether it shades, on the one hand, into just a proximity, or into a symbiotic relationship on the other.

3 Parasitism.
One organism, the parasite, gains from the association while the other, the host, is harmed. Here again there may be problems. Some organisms cause enough damage to the host to make their parasitic mode of life obvious, but often the harm done is minor and the parasite and host live in a long lasting association. After all, it is in the parasite's interest not to harm the host too severely or it will have to seek a new home.

As you can see, these three categories are not clear cut. Sometimes the relationships depend on particular morphological adaptations such as the lateral flattening of fleas, or the hooks and suckers on the head of the tapeworm. Very often the relationships come about because the behaviour patterns of the two organisms have evolved in a mutually adaptive way. Let us consider some of these inter-relating behaviour patterns.

MUTUALISM OR SYMBIOSIS

There are many insect examples of this type of relationship. Certain bugs, such as aphids and scale insects, produce a sweet liquid called honey dew from the phloem sap on which they feed. The sap contains sucrose, various amino acids, and some vitamins and minerals. During feeding the bugs pierce the sieve tubes in the phloem and then pump the sugary liquid into their alimentary canal. As the sap passes through the alimentary canal, about half of the amino acids, vitamins and minerals are absorbed, and part of the sugar, and the remaining, still very nutriti-ous, liquid passes out of the anus. Often the liquid just spreads onto the stem on which the bug is feeding making it very sticky. However in some bugs the honey dew solidifies and falls to the ground as scales, which are eaten by nomadic human tribes, and which formed the 'manna' from heaven which helped to feed the Israelites in the desert.

It is not surprising that during the evolution of such an extrava-gant, parasitic method of feeding by the bug on the plant, another organism should have adapted to 'cash in' on the excess material. Ants of various species have evolved behavioural and anatomical changes which enable them to feed on the honey dew. They stroke the bugs with their antennae, and this stimulates the bug to release the liquid. In some cases the bugs have lost all of their original protective structures, and depend entirely upon their ant partners for protection, repaying them with food. Some aphids have become almost like domestic cattle con-stantly tended and 'milked' by ants, and some are even cared for within ant nests. Eggs of the corn root aphis, *Aphis maidiracis*, are kept throughout the winter in the nest of the ant, *Lasius neoniger*, and the emergent nymphs are carried by the ants to the correct food plant where they are tended. Some of the aphids develop wings and fly away in the early summer, and if they land on plants near another ant colony they are adopted by these ants. In some ant species the relationship has proceeded a stage further; the queen carries a scale bug in her mandi-bles during her nuptial flight, which will be incorporated into the new colony.

This is a relationship between a parasitised plant which provides the raw materials, and two animal species. A rather similar situation is seen in the triangle of the large blue butterfly, *Maculinea arion*, the ant, *Myrmica*, and wild thyme plants in downland regions of England. The butterfly lays her eggs on the thyme plant, and the emerging larvae feed on the plant until they have carried out their third moult. Their behaviour and physiology then alter. Each larva has developed a honey gland, and if an ant approaches the larva adopts a peculiar position and allows the ant to 'milk' it. The ant then carries the larva to its nest, and there it is allowed to feed on the eggs and larvae of the ants, all the time producing the sugary 'honey' which the ants eat. The butterfly larva stays, protected and fed, within the ant's nest, and after pupation it emerges and flies away to mate, and if female, to lay eggs on a thyme plant as near to an ant's nest as possible.

Mixed species associations for mutual benefit are also found in vertebrates. The ox-pecker birds, *Buphagus* sp., spend their lives wandering over the hides of large, grazing animals in Africa; the birds feed on the ticks, lice and fleas on the skin, and the mammal benefits both by the reduction of its parasites, and by the advanced warning of predators given when the bird flies off.

The crocodile bird, *Pluvianus aegyptius*, enters the mouth of the crocodile and removes both the food stuck between its teeth, and any leeches which have fastened onto the mouth lining. The Galapagos iguana, *Conolophus subcristatus*, is cleaned by the small finches, *Geospiza fuliginosa* and *Geospiza fortis*. When the iguana sees the birds it raises itself high on its legs and lifts its tail so that the birds can get underneath.

Well over twenty species of fish are known to rid large fish of parasites in a similar cleaning symbiosis. The golden brown wrasse, *Oxyjulis californica*, from southern Californian waters, cleans the opal eye, *Girella nigricans*, which gather and wait in throngs for their 'wash and brush-up'. Most cleaner fish have evolved pointed snouts and teeth which enable them to pick off the parasites, sometimes even from inside the mouth of the larger fish. They are also mostly highly coloured and this seems to act as an advertising signal; as predatory fish leave them alone, these bright colours have been mimicked by other non-cleaning fish as a defensive method, or in some cases as a method of predation. (Figure 74 see next page) Sometimes large fish are cleaned by shrimps of the genera *Stenopus* and *Periclimenes* which crawl under the gill covers or into the mouth when the fish exhibits the appropriate 'inviting' signal.

What may be thought of as multiple factor symbiosis occurs in the mixed groups of herbivorous mammals found on the African plains, made up of various combinations of impala, wildebeest, gazelles, zebra and baboons. Each species is sensitive to the alarm behaviour of at least one of the others, and so the efficiency of their alarm system against predators is increased. It is also possible that such a grouping increases foraging efficiency, particularly in areas of low plant productivity as the

FIGURE 74

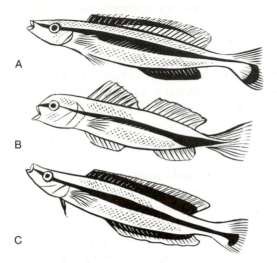

Colour patterns of two cleaner fish and a mimic.
A *Labroides dimidiatus.*
B *Elancatinus oceanops.*
These are small cleaners which are allowed to approach larger fish to rid them of ectoparasites.
C *Aspidontes taeniatus.*
This is a mimic of the cleaners which is also allowed to approach the larger fish. However when it gets near enough it bites pieces of flesh from the larger fish.

member species may have different food requirements, although often such a mixed group benefits only one or two of the species involved, and so is really an example of the next category.

COMMENSALISM

The hermit crab, *Eupagurus bernhardis*, lives with its soft abdomen tucked inside an empty whelk shell. Sometimes the colonial coelenterate *Hydractinia* is already attached to the whelk shell chosen by the crab. The coelenterate can obtain food particles left by the crab, and the crab also carries it around to different regions. So the coelenterate benefits in two ways and the crab gains nothing from the association.

Sponges are extremely simple animals which filter out small planktonic particles for food from water swept in through numerous pores in the body wall. The pores connect up with an internal canal system which has a few large exit holes. In its passage through the sponge the water leaves a coating of food particles on the walls of the canals; it also carries small organisms which may take up residence within the canal system. Many crustaceans become permanently imprisoned within sponges having stayed there until they are too large to escape through the exit holes. *Euplectella*, Venus' flower basket, and *Hyalonema*, the glass-rope sponge, both contain these commensal crustaceans. From the crustacean's viewpoint the arrangement is excellent; it is safe within the sponge and also has a constant stream of food brought to it.

PARASITISM

There are many different types of social parasitism in which one animal derives an advantage, and the other one loses.

Hyenas are great stealers of already killed animals, and they will often run behind packs of African hunting dogs and try to rob them of their kill. The 'law of the highwayman' applies to ants of an Indian species of the genus *Crematogaster* which ambush workers of the harvesting ant, *Monomorium*, as they are returning to the nest after harvesting expeditions, relieving them of the seeds they have collected.

The brood parasitism of the cuckoo is another way in which food is diverted into the 'wrong' animal.

One of the most dramatic examples of social parasitic behaviour is that of 'slave making' which has arisen in many ant species. Basically, during a slave raid workers will go out from the nest in a column, and will penetrate a colony of a closely related species. Here they capture pupae which they bring back to the nest. When the pupae emerge as adults, they take over the running of the nest, the parasitic owners doing little in the way of foraging, nest cleaning and brood rearing. The American ant, *Formica subintegra*, carries out such raiding parties many times a day, and produces a chemical which acts as an allomone to alarm and disperse the owner workers in the raided nest, and as a pheromone attracting the raiders. The chemical, a mixture of acetates, has long lasting effects within the raided nest, and frequently the original workers abandon it completely.

All of these inter-relationships have a common basis in that both organisms are present in the same place and at the same time, and their behavioural connections can be seen. However this is not always the case. As we have seen in Chapter 10, mimicry in which an animal species has adopted the colours, behaviour patterns, sounds or structure of another species is widespread. If it is the colour and shape that are copied, then the mimic is protected whether or not it is harmless and edible (Batesian mimicry) or poisonous and inedible like the model (Mullerian mimicry).

Certain spiders mimic ants, even to the extent of developing a 'waist' from the cephalo-thorax and moving in an ant-like zig-zag, their second pair of legs held aloft like antennae. Many insects mimic the black and yellow stripes of the stinging hymenopterans (bees and wasps). Even certain moths, the clearwings, have lost their normal wing scales and, although harmless themselves, have come to resemble the stinging hornets.

Man, of course, is the animal with the largest range of interspecific relationships. The farmer depends on sheep dogs to round up his mountain sheep; he imitates the sucking action of a calf in milking a cow either by hand or by machine; he alters the environment surrounding his domestic poultry so that they will lay more eggs for him to eat. Although in this century we have all come to depend on the internal combustion engine, before this we literally got the necessary horse power for our agricultural and other activities from the horse. There are signs that such a situation may well re-occur as we try to preserve our dwindling stocks of fossil fuels.

22 Behavioural genetics

Ever since man started to keep domesticated animals he has been engaged in selectively breeding for characteristics to fit his needs. Some of these characteristics were physical; he wanted pulling power in his oxen or horses, good wool in his sheep and goats, and plenty of milk from his cattle. Many desirable characteristics were behavioural however; man needed fierce aggression in his hunting dogs, but tameness and docility in his farm animals.

Most inherited behavioural characteristics are the phenotypic result of polygene systems, in which many genes work to produce not the either/or situation of Mendel's tall or short pea plants, but a 'more' or 'less' situation. Polygene systems tend to produce a normal distribution in a population. (Figure 75)

In such a normal distribution there is a wide range between the 'more' end and the 'less' end, and the standard way of selectively breeding from such a population is to mate together two animals with

FIGURE 75

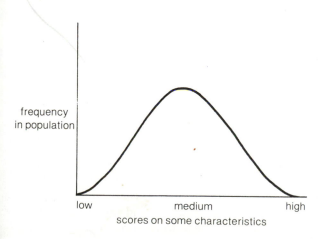

A frequency distribution in a polygene system. In a system involving six different genes, A, B, C, D, E and F, the highest score would depend on the presence of twelve dominant alleles, AA, BB, CC, DD, EE and FF, and the lowest on the presence of twelve recessive alleles, aa, bb, cc, dd, ee and ff.

the desired characteristics. So in a distribution showing aggression, one would mate two animals from the top extreme of the curve to try to produce a more aggressive strain, whereas to produce a docile strain one would mate animals from the lower end of the distribution.

Experiments such as this have been carried out in many organisms. The fruit fly, *Drosophila*, shows differences in spontaneous activity which were measured by placing individual flies in actographs for a fixed time under carefully standardised conditions, and recording the amount of movement. If selective mating is carried out at the low or high activity ends of the distribution, then resulting populations after fourteen generations differ vastly from a control, non-selected population. (Figure 76)

Manning carried out a similar breeding programme in *Drosophila melanogaster*, in which he selected for slow and fast mating speeds. He compared two fast strains, FA and FB, and two slow strains, SA and SB, with non-selected controls and found that after eighteen selected generations, 80% of the fast strain had mated before the slow strains had started. (Figure 77)

After twenty-five generations the average time for courtship ending in mating was about forty minutes in the slow strains, compared with only three minutes in the fast strains.

Single gene mutations have also been found to be responsible for behaviour differences, at least in organisms such as *Drosophila* where a particular behaviour pattern is stereotyped, and Bastock has studied the effect of particular mutations in *Drosophila* courtship. Most genes are pleiotropic, that is they have effects other than the main obvious one. Sometimes it is relatively easy to see how the obvious mutation can have secondary effects, but this is not so in other mutations. As we have seen in Chapter 17, the wing vibration of the male stimulates the female antennae during courtship behaviour and mutant males are less efficient at mating than wild type males. A bar eye mutation reduces the number of functional ommatidia and a white eye mutation reduces the pigment present in the eye of the male, and so it is not so efficient at seeing the female. Vestigial and dumpy wing mutations affect the shape and power of the wings, and therefore alter the possible vibration pattern. The connection between the mutation and the altered courtship pattern is relatively clear with these mutations. Yellow bodied males are also at a disadvantage, but as courtship also occurs in darkness it cannot be the sight of the body colour which matters. It is not yet clear how the yellow mutation works, but it is thought to have an effect on the central nervous system. Yellow males have the normal wing vibration frequency, but the bouts of vibration are shorter and the interval between them is longer than in the wild type males. The yellow

FIGURE 76

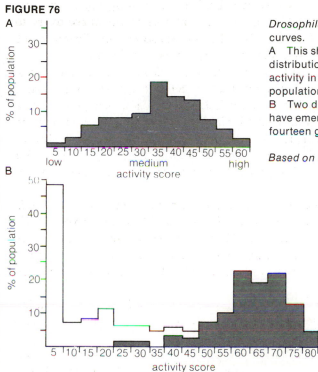

A

B

Drosophila spontaneous activity curves.
A This shows the frequency distribution of spontaneous activity in the original population.
B Two distinct populations have emerged after selection for fourteen generations.

Based on Connolly.

FIGURE 77

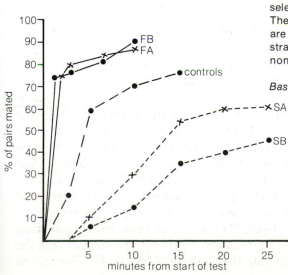

Curves to show mating speed in *Drosophila melanogaster* after eighteen generations of selection.
The two fast strains, FA and FB are compared with two slow strains, SA and SB, and with non-selected controls.

Based on Manning.

males take, on average, four minutes longer to carry the courtship pattern through to successful mating, and so their mating success when they are in competition with wild type males, is reduced.

So, in *Drosophila*, it is known that both single gene mutations, and polygene systems can have important behavioural effects.

Behaviour patterns in vertebrates tend to be more complicated and variable than the courtship pattern of *Drosophila*. Many studies have been based on inbred strains of mice. Inbreeding, that is brother/sister matings, carried out for many generations leads to populations in which certain alleles are fixed, and so individuals in the population resemble each other genotypically. (Figure 78)

This means that two homozygous strains can be directly compared and their behavioural differences can be linked to their genotypes.

Rodgers and McClearn used two different inbred strains of mice to investigate alcohol preference. One strain, C57black, given the choice of alcohol or water took in 98% of their total fluid in the form of 10% alcohol, whereas another strain, C3H/2, consumed no alcohol at all, preferring water. Crossing of these two strains produced mice which were intermediate in their alcohol preference, and fostering experiments showed that the preference was genetic and not environmental.

Fighting in mice was investigated in another study. Ginsberg and Allee studied fights between males of three different strains, C57black, C3agouti, and C albino. Two different strain males were put together in a neutral cage, and their level of aggression and fighting ability was observed. It was found that the C57black were the most, and the C albinos the least effective fighters, although non-heritable factors such as fatigue or body size also had an effect. Within each strain there were also environmental effects. Individual mice could be conditioned to be less aggressive as a result of repeated defeats, or could become more aggressive as a result of constant victories over more submissive mice.

FIGURE 78

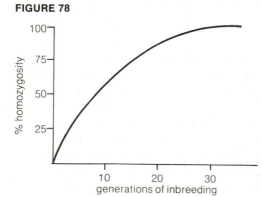

Curve to show the effect of inbreeding on genetic variability. The amount of genetic variability is reduced by many generations of inbreeding, leading to a population in which many genes are present in a homozygous condition.

Various other behaviour patterns have been studied with different inbred strains, such as the rapidity with which partially starved mice would eat, or their emotionality measured by the rate and amount of defaecation under stress, or the amount of exploratory behaviour shown.

Nest building by mice was investigated by van Oortmerssen. One strain of mice, CPB, fray and shred straw and paper to make a nest above ground and do not try particularly hard to avoid lighted areas. C57black mice do not shred nesting material, but prefer to dig holes and make a nest underground by pulling in nesting material. If forced to nest on the surface, they tried to find darkened areas. In crossing experiments between CPB (shredders) with C57black (non-shredders) the offspring showed intermediate levels of nest material shredding. Fostering experiments again showed the differences to be genetic rather than environmental, the offspring resembling their true, rather than their foster, parents.

However some studies by Southwick on aggression in mice have shown that cross fostering can have some effect. Aggression in male mice of two strains, A/J and CFW, was determined on three scales: the frequency of chase, attack and fight; the time taken to start an attack; the percentage of mice showing scars from previous injury. The two strains differed widely in their scores on these scales, A/J males being non-aggressive and taking a long time before attacking and the CFW males being highly aggressive with a very short latent period before they attacked. Some pups were cross-fostered with nursing mothers of the other strain; some were left with their own mothers as controls, and some were fostered within their own strain.

The scores these mice obtained when adult showed that the non-aggressive strain males became more aggressive when they were reared by aggressive, CFW, foster mothers. The reverse situation of aggressive CFW pups reared by non-aggressive A/J mothers did not result in a lessening of aggression in the CFW animals. However, even though the non-aggressive cross-fostered pups had become more aggressive, their score was still nowhere near that of the control aggressive animals. Fostering within the strain had very little effect on aggression.

These experiments have used male mice, and as we have seen earlier, it is usually the male animal which shows aggression. In many organisms, maleness is the result of the presence of a Y chromosome, the male being XY, the female XX. Occasionally, because of a fault in meiosis and fertilisation, animals develop with a doubling of the Y chromosome, and so they are XYY instead of XY. If aggression is basically a male characteristic primarily needed to repel intruders and to acquire a mate, and if the presence of the Y chromosome produces maleness, then one might expect heightened aggression in these XYY animals. Some work with aquarium fish, in which individuals may be YY without having the X chromosome, has shown that this occurs. YY individuals in competition with normal XY males for mates showed about a tenfold increase in both their courtship behaviour to the females, and their aggressive behaviour to the competing males.

As a doubling of the Y chromosome can also occur in man it has been thought that such XYY men would also be super-aggressive. Some studies of men who were inmates in maximum security hospitals for the mentally ill seemed to show an abnormally high proportion of men with this XYY pattern. In 1965 Jacobs and her colleagues investigated the chromosomal make-up of men in the Scottish State Hospital, and found that 3% of all the men had the XYY condition. These men were also taller, on average, than the other inmates; a finding which meant that many investigators have confined their sampling to tall men in further hospital studies.

A measure of the frequency of the XYY pattern in the total population has been found by a study of 11 680 new-born boys in Edinburgh, 14 of whom were XYY, and of 13 751 new-born boys in Boston, USA, 13 of whom also had the extra Y chromosome. A frequency of 0.1% means that there must be many men with the abnormal condition who do not show severe behavioural disturbances.

Although the 3% XYY men found by Jacobs is disproportionately large, and seemed to confirm the view that the extra Y chromosome had led to heightened aggression, this is not the whole story.

Studies of the inmates of Rampton and Moss Side, both English special hospitals, showed that out of 900 men, 21 had abnormal X chromosome patterns, 7 out of 21 being XXYY, the remaining 14 being XXY. This XXY frequency of 1.5% is also much higher than the 0.1% XXY people found in the general population.

The heightened aggression shown in these XXY men could not be thought to result from a double dose of the Y chromosome.

In mammals, at least, the X chromosome is physiologically much more important than the Y, coding for a number of enzymes needed for normal body functioning. The Y chromosome determines the development of the male reproductive organs. The presence of an extra X chromosome has severe phenotypic effects. XXY males are sterile and show some female characteristics such as breast development. As figure 79 page 177 shows, any abnormality in the number of sex chromosomes usually results in a lowered intelligence quotient, and this could partially account for the disproportionately large numbers of both XXY and XYY men in such hospitals for the mentally subnormal. (Figure 79)

FIGURE 79

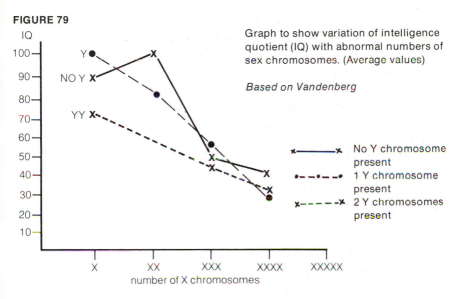

Graph to show variation of intelligence quotient (IQ) with abnormal numbers of sex chromosomes. (Average values)

Based on Vandenberg

A trisomic situation such as this, where three sex chromosomes rather than two are present, is the result of an accidental alteration of a gamete, and is not likely to be passed on from one generation to the next. The experiments with mice and *Drosophila* were carried out with highly inbred strains, and this is something it is impossible to match with people. Inbreeding leads to a high percentage of homozygosity and similarity of genotypes, and although close inbreeding does not happen in humans, a situation can occur in which identical genotypes are produced.

Monozygotic twins are derived from the splitting of a single zygote and so are genetically identical, and many investigations on the inheritance of particular behavioural characteristics, and how these are also affected by the environment, have been carried out with identical twins. To show how much of a particular characteristic, such as motor skill or the ability to do well in intelligence tests, is inherited and how much is the result of the environment, one needs to compare monozygotic twins with dizygotic twins who, as they have been derived from two different zygotes, are genetically dissimilar.

Such a comparison can be made if the members of the monozygotic and the dizygotic pairs are scored on their ability to carry out a particular test, and the score differences between the co-twins found. The difference between the dizygotic pair is due both to heredity and to environment; that between the monozygotic pair is due to environment alone. So by comparison one can estimate the importance of heredity in this particular characteristic.

This simple outline suggests that it is relatively easy to draw conclusions from such tests. However there are many possible sources of error. Monozygotic twins tend to be treated more alike by parents, siblings and friends, and also to spend more time together, than dizygotic twins. Their environment is therefore unlike that of dizygotic twins, even if these are in what appear to be similar family circumstances, and so a straight comparison becomes impossible.

However if the monozygotic twins have been separated early in life and reared separately, then it should be easier to deduce the relative importance of heredity and environmental factors. One of the great problems has been the small number of monozygotic twins reared in these unusual circumstances and available for study.

The main topic of investigation has been on IQ, the intelligence quotient. This is the ratio, expressed as a percentage, of a person's mental age (calculated from his ability to answer graded tests) to his actual age. The theory that IQ levels are largely inherited was based on four studies of separated monozygotic twins involving 122 pairs in total. Of these 122 pairs, 53 pairs were studied by the late Sir Cyril Burt. However there is now some evidence that his results are unreliable, and as the extent of the unreliability is difficult to assess, it is necessary to ignore Burt's data. This leaves only 69 pairs of twins, a very small number from which to draw conclusions. Also the changed environments necessary for the study did not apply to all of these twins; many were reared by close relatives or attended the same school as the co-twin, and so they shared rather similar environments.

As you can see, there are real problems involved in this subject. On the one hand, some geneticists and psychologists argue that, although it is impossible to set up scientifically controlled environments in which to rear separated twins, there is enough evidence to suggest that IQ, and, they think, other behavioural traits, are largely inherited. Other researchers think that what figures there are can justifiably point to a major role for the environment. The issue, of course, has sociological and political overtones. The phenotypic expression of a gene depends on the environment in which the genotype functions, and the interactions between genes and the environment are extremely complex. This being so, it would seem that altering the environment in the direction of social equality would satisfy not only the 'environmentalists' who claim the major role of the environment in determining intelligence, but also the 'hereditarians' who recognise that genes do not function in isolation from the environment.

The genotype, after all, determines only the potentialities of an organism. As Medawar says. 'Heredity proposes and development disposes'.

23 The evolution of behaviour

We have seen in the last chapter that selective breeding can result in the polarisation of a behaviour pattern in members of a population. Thus Manning could breed fast mating or slow mating individuals of *Drosophila melanogaster* with such a difference in courtship time that most of the fast maters had finished before the slow maters had begun. These two types were selected within the same species and so had the same basic courtship pattern, the only difference being in the time taken. *Drosophila*, being such a useful animal for genetic investigations, has been studied for over sixty years, and it is known that there are over two thousand species. With such a large number of species it is obvious that some must resemble each other very closely, and in fact many can only be identified by a comparison of internal structure shown by dissection. This does not seem to present any difficulty to courting *Drosophila* however.

A species is a collection of organisms with a common gene pool which is sexually isolated from another species with a different gene pool. In other words, members of a species can recognise and mate with conspecifics, but do not mate with members of other species. As the different species of *Drosophila* may look very similar, it is likely that there is some difference in the courtship behaviour which stops interspecific mating.

At least forty species of *Drosophila* have a courtship display which looks identical to us, and as the females can accept the right males in the dark, visual stimulation does not appear to be the discriminating factor. As we have seen, the male vibrates his wings rapidly during courtship and this produces air movements which stimulate the arista on the antennae of the female. The arista and the distal joint of the antenna vibrate with a natural resonance of about 200 Hz, and it has been found that this is the wing beat frequency of *Drosophila* flight, although the pattern of sound produced in flight is very complex. Different species seem to have used the fundamental flight wing movements in different ways during courtship to give altered frequency or pulse patterns. So *Drosophila melanogaster* males emit pulses of 330 Hz twenty-nine times a second, whereas *Drosophila simulans* males (a morphologically very close species) emit the same frequency notes but only twenty times a second. Other closely related species produce the same frequency note but at different pulse rates. Another collection of closely related species form the *obscura* group; in these the basic frequency is 500 Hz and their pulse rates vary. Although the number of variations is rather limited, it has been found that if the songs are very similar, then the flies are morphologically rather distinct, and so discrimination can still occur.

So a slight alteration in a fundamental behaviour pattern can lead to speciation, and once sexual isolation has occurred, further inter-specific differences may evolve.

The courtship pattern of *Drosophila* is behaviourally quite simple. Vertebrate courtship displays have many different elements, some of which are ritualised activities from other behavioural contexts. There is, therefore, more scope for alterations in this original pattern to lead to speciation, and this is shown very clearly in the various species of birds which make up the Anatinae, that is, the ducks.

Ducks show marked sexual differences in appearance, the females usually being dull brown, whereas the males develop colourful plumage during the breeding season. Pair bonding lasts for a comparatively short time, and each bird has several mates during its lifetime. The female chooses her new mate during a prolonged period of social courtship in which several drakes participate. Many different species may share over-wintering areas, and in these species the courtship displays are elaborate and so inter-specific matings are reduced.

Just as courtship behaviour in *Drosophila* is of a certain pattern with specific variations of song, there is an underlying pattern of courtship in all the species which make up the Anatinae. Many elements of this basic pattern have started as displacement activities or intention movements, and these have been adapted into ritual movements, some of which have been accompanied in evolution by the development of changed morphological structures. One of the courtship movements found in ducks is ritual preening, in which the drake briefly touches its wing with its beak. The touched section of the wing is made up of brightly coloured feathers, forming the speculum, and the colour and form of the speculum varies from the rich blue stripe of the mallard, to the much enlarged orange flag like structure found in the mandarin drake.

The mallard is a relatively primitive duck, and its behaviour patterns are known in most detail. Lorenz has analysed courtship behaviour in the mallard into various separate displays. (Figures 80 and 81)

Female behaviour includes inciting her mate to attack other males, the repulsion of strange males, and darting around and between displaying males in what is called 'nod-swimming'.

Male behaviour is much more complicated, and has many different displays. The most common display is the 'grunt-whistle' in which the bird rears up in the water, and then plunges its head down as if it is going to drink. The neck is then straightened and a sharp whistle followed by a grunt are emitted.

FIGURE 80

A

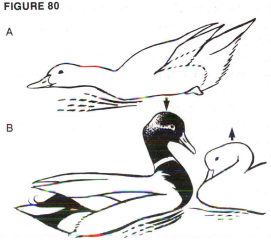

B

FIGURE 81

A

A

B

C

C

FIGURES 80 & 81

Some of the courtship movements shown by mallards.
Figure 80
Female movements.
A   The female mallard 'nod-swimming'. She keeps her head low on the surface of the water.
B   'Pumping'. This precedes copulation. The drake and the duck face each other and move their heads up and down.
Figure 81
Male movements.
A   Two movements from the 'grunt whistle' display.
B   The 'head up – tail up' posture. The wings and tail are lifted and the head is held high. This usually follows a 'grunt whistle' display.
C   Two movements from the 'down – up' display. This is the least common display. The drake looks as if it is going to drink; its breast is low in the water and its tail is held up. It then suddenly throws its head up and whistles.

Elements of this behaviour can be seen in an altered form in different species of ducks, although the basic mallard pattern is still recognisable. Originally only a small behaviour change would be needed to produce sexual isolation and speciation would then follow. (Figure 82)

FIGURE 82
A male North American Ruddy Duck displaying to two females. The male holds his tail up, and there are bubbles on the water from the movement of his breast.

Photograph by B. Gadsby   *Photograph by courtesy of the Wildfowl Trust, Martin Mere.*

The patterns of displacement preening or displacement drinking originally arose from the internal conflict in the males between the tendency towards sexual or attack behaviour and the opposing tendency to escape. Those males which could more efficiently perform the displacement patterns were more successful in mating. It is likely that the patterns caught the attention of the famale and perhaps also sexually stimulated her. A similar conflict between attack and escape tendencies is seen in the original pattern of inciting shown in the female. The patterns were then ritualised and altered in various ways and this led to sexual isolation. However the patterns lost their dependence on the internal conflict and have become an almost invariable part of courtship. This movement of the patterns away from their original controlling mechanisms has been named emancipation by Tinbergen.

It is important in any type of communication that the signals involved must be recognisable and unambiguous if they are to be effective. So behaviour patterns which become ritualised are simplified in form and often involve exaggerated movements. The form is maintained even though the strength of the stimulus varies. The behaviour pattern may be held for a brief period if stimulation is weak, or for a longer period in response to strong stimulation but the pattern itself is performed at a fixed intensity. This makes it more clearly recognisable and Morris has named such a fixed response strength the 'typical intensity' for the particular behaviour pattern.

Courtship behaviour, whether in the original or in the altered new species' form, would be selected on the basis of its efficiency in producing a satisfactory reproductive outcome.

One of the bases of the theory of natural selection is that it is a process which ensures that some members of a population produce more offspring than others, their genes therefore appearing with greater frequency in the next generation. This being so, one would expect an organism to behave entirely to its own advantage; to acquire, by one means or another, as long and as efficient a reproductive life as possible, and to do this to the disadvantage of all the other members of the population. However many animals do not behave in this way. Some show altruistic behaviour which is helpful to other individuals, and which could be harmful to themselves.

Sometimes it is relatively easy to see how this altruism could have arisen. A female bird may draw the attention of a predator to herself by means of a distraction display; behaviour which, although it puts her at some risk, increases the chance of survival of her offspring. A 'distraction display' gene could therefore be selected for; without it the adult and the young, and of course their genes, could all be eliminated by predation.

Although a distraction display is a very obvious piece of altruistic behaviour, the whole business of rearing offspring may involve an enormous energy investment, particularly on the part of the mother. It does, however, help to ensure that her genes are passed on to surviving members of the next generation.

There are other altruistic behaviour patterns which do not directly benefit the offspring of the animal concerned. A warning call given by a bird which has seen a predator has the effect of making other birds in the flock remain motionless, and so less likely to be seen and attacked. The call, however, could draw attention to the bird which makes it, rendering it more vulnerable. If there is an altruistic gene for making warning calls, one might expect an animal possessing it, (and so also the gene), to be eliminated from the population. The deciding factor as to whether the gene will be eliminated, or will spread throughout the population is not whether the behaviour is useful to the animal carrying it out, but whether it is useful to the gene. If the flock of birds is made up of close relatives of the altruistic bird, then it is likely that some of them will also carry the altruistic gene. So the loss of one bird could be offset by the survival of many, with the subsequent spread of the altruistic genes in the population. The closer the relationship (kinship) between the animals, the more likely it is that altruistic behaviour would evolve.

In a sexually reproducing diploid species, the mother and father each pass on half their genes to an offspring. Siblings, on average, will have half their genes in common; half of those they inherited from the mother, and half of those they inherited from the father. So from the gene's position, it is as useful for an animal to be altruistic to its siblings as to its offspring. The altruistic genes will spread by 'kin selection' – a term suggested by Maynard Smith for the way in which a particular characteristic is established because of its effects on the survival of relatives of the animal possessing the gene.

'Kin selection' can also explain the altruistic behaviour patterns found in the honey bee, where workers carry out potentially suicidal attacks on intruders into the hive.

As we have seen in Chapter 16, honey bees have three castes. Queens and workers are diploid females which develop from fertilised eggs, and drones are haploid males which develop from unfertilised eggs. As males are haploid, the spermatozoa they make contain the full complement of their genes. Any diploid egg laid by the queen therefore contains half of her genes, but all of the father's genes. Sister workers have, on average, half of their mother's genes in common, as in the normal diploid situation, but as they all have all of their father's genes, they have a total of three quarters of their genes in common. Female worker bees therefore preserve their own genes better by maintaining and safeguarding their sisters in the hive, than in producing their own offspring.

So although at first sight it looks improbable, altruism is one way in which genes 'ensure' their 'immortality', and increase their frequency in future generations. Altruism is thus an adaptive characteristic – a characteristic which is maintained in a population by selection.

There are many other examples of behaviour which appear at first to be non-adaptive, and yet which have been selected during evolution. Homosexual pairings, or mock pairings, seem to be time consuming, reproductively useless, behaviour and yet they occur in many species. In macaques mounting of one male by another is a common ritual, but its value is to show a dominance order, the dominant animal mounting the subordinate. In the South American leaf fish, *Polycentrus schomburgkii*, subordinate males behave in a female manner when they approach dominant, territorial males. The females enter the territory of the male, and then by turning upside down leave their eggs on the lower surface of objects in the water. The male subsequently swims to the eggs to deposit sperm. The male 'mock females' accompany the real females to the point of laying their eggs, and might, therefore manage to put their own sperm near the eggs before being chased out by the dominant male.

So behaviour which appears at first to be non-adaptive may, in fact, turn out to be useful.

24 Epilogue

Man is, it appears, the dominant animal on the world at present. His evolution has produced a gradual increase in both the number of neurones in his nervous system, and the number of possible neural interconnections, and so he is no longer tied to the stimulus/response rigidity shown by many of the other animals.

There have been three historic definitions of man. First of all, man is a speaking animal. As we have seen, many other animals make vocal communication sounds. However most of these sounds arise directly from the animal's need and behaviour at the time, and the information they impart is very limited. Man has acquired the capacity to extend his vocalisations into objective sounds, which he uses to categorise his surroundings.

Man is also a social animal, and this, of course, is implied by the first definition. Vast numbers of species other than *Homo sapiens* are social. Sometimes their societies are rigidly determined both by inherited and nutritional factors as in the social insects; other societies may be preserved and maintained by various types of dominance hierarchies. Man has social inter-relationships of many types, and at various levels.

The third definition of man is that he is a tool making and using animal, and here again it is now known that this characteristic applies to other animals also.

So we have our three historic definitions, none of which applies solely to man, and we must look further to establish what distinguishes him from the other animals.

Certain changes have occurred during evolution which have had enormously far reaching effects. One such change was the evolution of photosynthetic mechanisms which could break down water and liberate oxygen into the atmosphere in sufficient quantities to form an ozone layer which could then shield land organisms against lethal cosmic radiation.

The history of man shows another important evolutionary alteration. The evolution of man's large cerebral hemispheres with their millions of neurones and complicated circuitry enabled him to conceptualise; to reason things out; to solve problems by thinking out an approach and then to act on the basis of insight. He could adapt his behaviour directly to new external conditions without the energetically wasteful procedure of 'trial and error'. His bipedal gait, and the free pair of legs that this gave him, enabled him to extend and refine his manipulatory skill and he could begin to adapt the environment to fit his own needs.

His whole pattern of evolution changed from that based on genetic inheritance to that based on social transmission. Each generation could learn something new about the environment, and because of the evolution of speech, such information could be passed on to subsequent generations. With the invention of written language man could begin to educate by precept, rather than by example. In each generation the stock of culture and information would increase. Children are born today with no more genetic information than the earliest children; what they do have is thousands of years of accumulated knowledge which enables them to carry out an enormous variability of behaviour during their life span. Without such accumulated knowledge, each generation would have to start back at the base line of human cultural evolution.

Although the date of the emergence of tool using man is being pushed further and further back as new fossils are found, it is only ten thousand years since man began to domesticate plants and animals. From then on, the rate of cultural progress accelerated and the ever growing stock of knowledge allowed man to invent the machines without which our present modern life would be impossible.

The sense organs man possesses can be outclassed by those of many other species; however his microscopes and telescopes, his radios and amplifiers, have extended their range enormously. Man is capable of moving through the air, on land, or on or under water. His ecological range is vast; he can survive in different climates by the addition or removal of clothing.

So we see that man has taken a fundamentally different path from that taken by other animals in his evolutionary history, and it is as a result of this that we can sit and read books on animal behaviour.

Experiments

CHAPTER 3

A   Response to light by Euglena

Requirements:
Euglena culture
Small beaker
Piece of black paper large enough to surround beaker, with slit cut in it.

Place the *Euglena* culture in the beaker which is then surrounded by the black paper, and covered by a black paper lid. Leave in daylight. On removing the paper a faint green line will be seen in the region which received light through the slit, showing an accumulation of *Euglena*.

B   Light receptors of earthworms

Requirements:
A large active earthworm
Wax dissecting tray
Pieces of thick cardboard

Rinse the earthworm in water and place it in the centre of the dissecting tray, dorsal side uppermost (the dorsal surface is usually darker than the ventral, has no projecting chaetae, and shows the dorsal blood vessel as a dark line). Shade the anterior end of the worm with a piece of cardboard and see how long it takes before the worm moves into the darkness. Repeat, but this time shade the posterior end of the worm. Is there any difference in the time taken? Does this suggest that the photo-receptors are more concentrated in one area?

C   Temperature receptors in human skin

Requirements:
Blunt needle

Explore the surface of the skin by gently prodding with a blunt needle.

In particular places, coldness or warmth may be felt. Compare the numbers of sensitive spots in equal areas of skin on the back and the palm of the hands, the inside and outside of the forearm, the elbow and the wrist. Is there any biological basis for testing the temperature of a baby's bath by dipping the elbow into the water; or testing the temperature of the baby's bottle by holding it against the inner surface of the forearm?

D   Chemoreceptors in blowflies

Requirements:
Adult blowflies (these can easily be obtained from maggots bought at a fishing tackle shop). The blowflies should have been able to drink distilled water for 12 hours before the experiment starts.
0.25M sucrose solution
Ether, or a carbon dioxide supply
A sheet of white, non-absorbent paper

Lightly anaesthetise the flies, either with ether or with carbon dioxide, and cut off the wings near to the thorax. Remove the forelegs from some of the flies, also. Allow all the flies to recover. While they are recovering prepare the sheet of paper by drawing two concentric circles, the inner one with distilled water, the outer with the sucrose solution. Place a fly in the centre of the rings. Note its behaviour when it reaches the ring of distilled water, and when it reaches the ring of sucrose solution. Repeat with other flies. Does removing the forelegs have any effect on the behaviour of the flies?

CHAPTER 5

Domestic or laboratory animals may be watched to see what use they make of territorial pheromones.

If you have a male dog which you accompany for walks, you will be accustomed to making slow progress. Each lamp-post, or gatepost, on your path will first be sniffed, and then urinated on, by your dog. When you next take him for a walk, consider his actions, and those of the dogs he meets, as those of territorial antagonists, and see how much more you can learn of canine behaviour.

CHAPTER 7

A Flying reflexes in the blowfly
Requirements:
Blowflies
Ether or carbon dioxide supply
Nail varnish
A piece of cotton thread about 50 cm long

Lightly anaesthetise the blowflies with ether or carbon dioxide, and then carefully attach the cotton thread to the dorsal surface of the thorax by a small drop of nail varnish. Try to place the cotton so that it does not unbalance the fly, or interfere with its wing movements. Allow the fly to recover. If the fly is then lifted from the bench, it will begin to fly. Flying will stop if its feet are touched by a piece of paper. Blowing on the blowfly will usually stimulate it to fly while it is suspended.

B Human reflexes
a The knee-jerk reflex.
Sit comfortably with one leg crossed over the other at the knee. If your partner now sharply taps the patellar tendon with the side of his hand, there will be a sudden contraction of the quadriceps muscle of that leg, producing an obvious knee jerk.

b The iris reflex.
Your partner covers his eyes with his cupped hands, keeping his eyes open.

After a period of time to allow his eyes to become dark adapted, he takes his hands away from his eyes. What do you notice about the iris, and how is this useful?

In a variation of this experiment, the subject stands with his back to a window and his hands held about 5 cm in front of his eyes, thereby shielding them from some light. By watching from the side, see what happens to the iris of the right eye if the left eye is suddenly stimulated by light because of the removal of the left hand from its earlier position. How does the iris reflex differ from the knee-jerk reflex?

c The gagging reflex.
Examine the back of the mouth by using a mirror. Notice the uvula, the fleshy downgrowth at the back of the soft palate. Gently touch this with a piece of clean paper which may be longitudinally folded to make it rather stiffer. What happens to the soft palate, and to the back of the tongue? Can you think of a purpose for this reflex?

C Responses to variations in humidity in woodlice
Requirements:
Choice chamber
Drying agent such as anhydrous calcium chloride
Dry, blue cobalt thiocyanate papers
About 20 woodlice
See diagram page 53

Collect a large number of woodlice from under stones, or under rotting wood. Set up the choice chamber, and leave it to establish a humidity gradient while you are sorting your woodlice. There are five common British species of woodlice which are easily distinguished by body shape, colour and size. Try to choose experimental animals of the same species, as the species differ in their response to varying humidity. Test the humidity gradient within the choice chamber by quickly dropping pieces of cobalt thiocyanate paper in to various sections, rapidly closing the apparatus again, and timing how quickly they change from blue to pink. Place five woodlice through each of the four holes in the lid, quickly reseal, and then count the number of woodlice in each section of the apparatus at fixed time intervals. The experiment can be repeated, but using only one woodlouse and watching its movements to see if there is a change in the turning rate in different humidities. It may be that the woodlouse you have chosen just walks round and round the dish in the angle between the wall and the gauze, and this response to contact is called thigmotaxis. The thigmotactic response interferes with the klinokinetic response you are trying to demonstrate, and it may be necessary to try a few woodlice before you find one which walks across the centre of the chamber.

D Response of blowfly maggots to light
Requirements:
Blowfly maggots a few days before they are due to pupate
Sheet of dark coloured paper
2 lamps containing equal power bulbs

The maggots should be dark adapted by having been kept in the dark for a few days. (Maggots bought from fishing tackle shops may be kept in a juvenile state for many weeks in a ventilated tin of sawdust in a domestic refrigerator.) Place the paper on the bench and then position the two lamps so that their beams are at right angles across the paper. Make the room as dark as possible, and then place the maggots on the paper. Switch on one lamp and watch the response made by the maggots. Then switch on the second lamp, switching off the first. When the maggots have responded to the new direction of light, switch on the first lamp again and note the response to the two lights. Vary the intensity of one lamp by moving it closer to the maggots. Is

there any change in the direction of movement? Observe carefully and decide what type of orientation movement the maggots are making.

CHAPTER 8

There may be many opportunities for you to observe the development of behaviour patterns in human babies and toddlers. Whenever you see a mother with a small baby, notice if she has it cradled in her left or right arm. Look at photographs, paintings and magazines and try to decide if left arm cradling is really more common.

CHAPTER 9

A Habituation in the earthworm
Requirements:
Large, active earthworm
Wax dissecting tray
Piece of thick cardboard large enough to cover tray

Place the rinsed earthworm on the dissecting tray and cover with the cardboard. After ten seconds remove the cardboard and note any response made by the worm. Cover the dish again and remove the cardboard ten seconds later. Continue in this way for a time. Does the worm habituate to the sudden light stimulus?
To see if the earthworm habituates to mechanical stimulation, gently prod it in the head with a blunt needle at ten second intervals. Does the withdrawal response eventually disappear?

B Habituation in the garden snail
Requirements:
Large active garden snail
Wax dissecting tray

Place the snail on the dissecting tray and wait until it has its posterior tentacles (on the top of its head) extended. Then shake the dish. If the tentacles are withdrawn, and then extended again, repeat at suitable short time intervals. If the tentacles are not withdrawn to shaking, try touching one gently with a brush. See how long it takes the snail to habituate to the stimulus used.

CHAPTER 10

A A simple Skinner box for a small mammal
Requirements:
A cardboard shoe box
A matchbox
Some sunflower seeds
A gerbil which has been without food for the previous 12–24 hours, although it has had water

Skinner boxes are mechanically complicated, but an adequate, non-automatic substitute can be used to demonstrate the principles of operant conditioning.

Remove the lid from the shoe box and glue a match-box to the bottom of the inner surface of one end. Have a supply of sunflower seeds available. Place the gerbil in the box at the other end, and watch it carefully. It will move around the box, sniffing the cardboard. When, by chance, it touches the matchbox – decide whether you are going to count a paw touch or a nose touch – drop a sunflower seed very close to the gerbil. Allow it to eat the sunflower seed, and then remove the gerbil and any seed husks. Repeat after a short time. Does the gerbil learn to go to touch the matchbox in the required way with repeated training? Try the experiment with rats, or mice.

B Maze training with small mammals.
Requirements:
A maze
Some concentrated food pellets
An untrained gerbil which has been without food for the 24 hours before the experiment
Stopwatch

A box maze with wooden sides at least 10 cm high and 50 cm long, and with internal polystyrene partitions, is made. The internal arrangement must give the animal a series of choice points where it could turn either to the left or the right. Decide that one end of the maze is always to be the food point, and place a food pellet there. Place the animal in the other end and then time it, and count the number of errors made, during its journey to the food. Allow it to eat for a short time and then return it to the beginning of the maze. Repeat the timing and error count. Run as many trials as you can in the time available. Plot two graphs, in each of which the number of trials is the horizontal axis. The vertical axis is the time taken, or the number of errors made. Did your experimental animal learn to run the maze? Do you think that the reinforcement provided by the food will be as strong at the end of the experiment as it is at the beginning? Is this offset by the possibility that the animal can get to the food more quickly?

C Human maze training
Requirements:
A maze made from sticking matchsticks to a sheet of cardboard. The maze may contain about 10 choice points. The matchsticks should make a path just wide enough for an index finger to move between
A stopwatch

Work with a partner who will time you and score your errors. You can either be blindfolded or you must keep your eyes closed. Make a series of trials running your finger through the maze path from the entrance to the exit point. Does your performance, measured by the time you take or the numbers of errors made, improve with practice? What do you consider to be the reward or reinforcement in this experiment?

CHAPTER 12

A Attention in humans

For this experiment work in groups of three. Two members of the group read different passages aloud and simultaneously to the third member, who tries to get the gist of what they are saying. Is it possible to do? Does it depend on the complexity of the passages, or the tone of voice, or the loudness? If you decide that different voices have an effect, try repeating the experiment with recordings made by one person, and replayed simultaneously through two tape recorders. Do repetition and familiarisation help? Is it really possible to concentrate on two things at once, like reading a book while listening to the radio, or does the brain keep alternating between the two? In the confused noise pattern which occurs at a party where everyone is engaged in conversation, one can be suddenly 'switched on' to a distant conversation on hearing one's own name mentioned, and this suggests that the brain is constantly monitoring the confused incoming signals, selecting for attention those which appear to be relevant.

B A changed learning situation in humans

Requirements:
Drawings of six-pointed stars
A mirror
Either a mirror stand or some 'plasticine'
A stopwatch

Diagram A

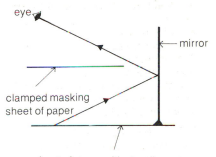

sheet of paper with star diagrams

Prepare a sheet of paper with four star diagrams. Position the mirror upright at one side of the paper, and clamp another sheet of paper so that the star diagrams may not be seen directly, but only by looking in the mirror. Try to draw around the star pattern, in the space **between** the two lines. Your partner should measure the time you take to make a complete circuit. Repeat with the other three star diagrams. Count the number of times your pencil point touched, or crossed, the two bordering lines. Did your performance improve with more trials? Why is this such a difficult task for many people? What do you think was happening between your eyes, brain and arm if you got 'stuck' at any point?

References

GENERAL REFERENCES

R. Ardrey, (1967)
The Territorial Imperative. (Collins.)

P. P. G. Bateson, R. A. Hinde, (Editors) (1976)
Growing Points in Ethology. (Cambridge University Press.)

L. A. Borradaile, Eastham, Potts and Saunders, (1961)
The Invertebrata. (Cambridge University Press. 4th Ed.)

L. O. Bjorn, (1976)
Light and Life. (Hodder and Stoughton.)

J. Bowlby, (1971)
Attachment. (Penguin Books.)

R. Buchsbaum, (1972)
Animals without Backbones. (Penguin Books.)

J. D. Carthy, (1966)
The Study of Behaviour. Studies in Biology, 3. (Edward Arnold.)

V. G. Dethier, and E. Stellar, (1970)
Animal Behaviour. Foundations of Modern Biology Series. (Prentice-Hall Inc. 3rd Ed.)

D. A. Dewsbury, (1978)
Comparative Animal Behaviour. (McGraw Hill.)

I. Eibl-Eibesfeldt, (1975)
Ethology, the Biology of Behaviour. (Holt, Rinehart & Winston Inc. 2nd Ed.)

S. M. Evans, (1968)
Studies in Invertebrate Behaviour. (Heinemann Educational Books, Ltd.)

R. L. Gregory, (1966)
Eye and Brain – the psychology of seeing. World University Library. (Weidenfeld and Nicolson.)

H. W. Grenville, (1971)
Biology of the Individual. The Principles of Modern Biology Series. (Longman.)

R. A. Hinde, (1970)
Animal Behaviour. (McGraw Hill. 2nd Ed.)

J. van Lawick-Goodall, (1968)
The Behaviour of free-living chimpanzees in the Gombe Stream Reserve. *Animal Behaviour Monographs* **1**. 161–311.

K. Z. Lorenz, (1970)
King Solomon's Ring. (Methuen. 2nd Ed.)

A. Manning, (1972)
An Introduction to Animal Behaviour. (Edward Arnold. 2nd Ed.)

J. Maynard Smith, (1969)
The Theory of Evolution. (Penguin Books. 2nd Ed.)

P. B. Medawar, (1969)
The Art of the Soluble. (Penguin Books.)

J. A. Ramsay, (1968)
Physiological Approach to the Lower Animals. (Cambridge University Press. 2nd Ed.)

M. B. V. Roberts, (1972)
Biology, a Functional Approach. (Nelson. 2nd Ed.)

J. P. Scott, (1972)
Animal Behaviour. (University of Chicago Press. 2nd Ed.)

C. U. M. Smith, (1970)
The Brain – Towards an Understanding. (Faber and Faber.)

W. H. Thorpe, (1963)
Learning and Instinct in Animals. (Methuen. 2nd Ed.)

N. Tinbergen, (1951)
The Study of Instinct. (Oxford Clarendon Press.)

P. N. R. Usherwood, (1973)
Nervous Systems. Studies in Biology, 36. (Edward Arnold.)

A. E. Vines, and N. Rees, (1972)
Plant and Animal Biology. Vols. 1 and 2. (Pitman. 4th Ed.)

V. B. Wigglesworth, (1964)
The Life of Insects. (Weidenfeld and Nicolson.)

E. O. Wilson, (1975)
Socio-biology, the New Synthesis. (Harvard University Press.)

Dennis W. Wood, (1974)
Principles of Animal Physiology. Contemporary Biology Series. (Edward Arnold. 2nd Ed.)

J. Z. Young, (1971)
An Introduction to the Study of Man. (Oxford University Press.)

REFERENCES CHAPTER 2

P. J. Mill, (1975)
The Organisation of the Nervous System in Annelids.
Simple Nervous Systems. Eds. P. N. R. Underwood and D. R. Newth. (Edward Arnold.)

C. L. Ralph, (1978)
Introductory Animal Physiology. (McGraw Hill.)

REFERENCES CHAPTER 3

B. U. Budelmann, (1977)
Statocyst Angular Acceleration Receptors.
The Biology of Cephalopods. Eds. M. Nixon and J. B. Messenger (Academic Press.)

H. W. Lissmann, (1963)
Electric Location by Fishes.
Scientific American. March, **208**.

R. Wehner, (1976)
Polarised-Light Navigation by Insects
Scientific American. July, **235**.

K. D. Roeder, (1965)
Moths and Ultrasound.
Scientific American. April, **212**.

REFERENCES CHAPTER 4

E. A. Beeman, (1947)
The Effects of Male Hormone on Aggressive Behaviour in Mice.
Physiological Zoology. **20**, 373–405.

J. Harker, (1964)
The Physiology of Diurnal Rhythms. (Cambridge University Press.)

G. A. Lincoln, F. Guiness, R. V. Short, (1972)
The Way in Which Testosterone Controls the Social and Sexual Behaviour of the Red Deer Stag, *Cervus elephas*.
Hormones and Behaviour. **3**, 375–396.

W. Loher, F. Huber, (1966)
Nervous and Hormonal Control of Sexual Behaviour in a Grasshopper (*Gomphocerus rufus*).
Symp. Soc. Exp. Biol. **20**, 381–400.

R. P. Michael, (1960)
An investigation into the sensitivity of circumscribed neurological areas to hormone stimulation by means of the application of oestrogens directly to the brain of the cat.
4th International Neurochemical Symposium. (Pergamon Press.)

E. N. Sassenrath, (1970)
Increased Adrenal Responsiveness Related to Social Stress in Rhesus Monkeys.
Hormones and Behaviour. **1**, 283–297.

H. Selye, (1956)
The Stress of Life. (McGraw Hill.)

R. Thomas, L. H. Finlayson, (1970)
Initiation of Circadian Rhythms in Arrhythmic Churchyard Beetles, *Blaps mucronata. Nature*. **228**, 577–578.

M. X. Zarrow, V. H. Denenberg, B. D. Sachs, (1972)
Hormones and Maternal Behaviour in Mammals.
Hormones and Behaviour. Ed. S. Levine. (Academic Press.)

REFERENCES CHAPTER 5

H. M. Bruce, (1966)
Smell as an exteroceptive factor.
Journal of Animal Science. suppl. **25**, 83–89.

C. G. Butler, R. K. Callow,
J. R. Chapman, (1964)
9-hydroxydec-trans-2-enoic acid, a
pheromone stabilizing honey bee
swarms.
Nature. **201.4920**, 733.

M. McClintock, (1971)
Menstrual synchrony and suppression.
Nature. **229.5282**, 244.

D. Schneider, (1969)
Insect Olfaction: Deciphering System
for Chemical Messages.
Science. **163**, 1031–1037.

S. Van Der Lee, L. M. Boot, (1955)
Spontaneous Pseudopregnancy in
Mice.
Acta Physiol. et Pharmacol. Neerland.
43.3, 442–444.

W. K. Whitten, F. H. Bronson, (1970)
The role of pheromones in
mammalian reproduction.
*Advances in chemoreception. Vol 1 –
Communication by chemical signals.*
Ed. Johnston, Moulton and Turk.
309–325. (Appleton-Century-Crofts,
N.Y.)

REFERENCES CHAPTER 6

F. H. Barnwell, (1963)
Observations on Daily and Tidal
Rhythms in Some Fiddler Crabs from
Equatorial Brazil.
Biological Bulletin. **125**, 399–415.

W. P. Colquhoun, (1971)
*Biological Rhythms and Human
Performance.* (Academic Press, New
York.)

K. Hoffmann, (1960)
Experimental Manipulation of the
Orientation Clock in Birds. Biological
Clocks.
*Cold Spring Harbour Symposium
Quantitative Biology.* **25**, 379–387.

E. Naylor, (1963)
Temperature Relationships of the
Locomotor Rhythm of *Carcinus.*
Journal Exp. Biol. **40**, 669–679.

REFERENCES CHAPTER 7

G. P. Baerends, (1959)
The Ethological Analysis of
Incubation Behaviour.
Ibis. **101**, 357–368.

N. Tinbergen, (1953)
Social Behaviour in Animals.
(Methuen.)

N. Tinbergen, A. C. Perdeck, (1950)
On the Stimulus Situation Releasing
the Begging Response in the Newly
Hatched Herring Gull Chick (*Larus
argentatus*).
Behaviour. **3**, 1–38.

REFERENCES CHAPTER 8

L. Carmichael, (1926)
The Development of Behaviour in
Vertebrates Experimentally Removed
from the Influence of External
Stimuli.
Psychological Review. **33**, 51–58.

G. Gottlieb, (1968)
Prenatal Behaviour of Birds.
Quarterly Review Biology. **43**,
148–174.

H. Harlow, (1959)
Love in Infant Monkeys.
Scientific American. June **200**.

M. Impekoven, (1973)
The Response of Incubating
Laughing Gulls (*Larus atricilla*) to
Calls of Hatching Chicks.
Behaviour. **46**.

D. Krech, (1965)
Morphological Alterations of the
Cerebral Cortex and Their Possible
Role in the Loss and Acquisition of
Information.
The Anatomy of Memory. Vol. 1. Ed.
D. P. Kimble. 88–139. (Palo Alto
Science and Behaviour Books.)

S. Levine, G. C. Haltmeyer,
G. G. Karas, V. H. Denenberg, (1967)
Physiological and Behavioural Effects
of Infant Stimulation.
Physiol. Behav. **2**, 55–59.

M. R. Rosenzweig, E. L. Bennett,
M. C. Diamond, (1972)
Brain Changes in Response to
Experience.
Scientific American. February, **226**.

M. A. Vince, (1969)
Embryonic Communication,
Respiration and the Synchronisation
of Hatching.
Bird Vocalisations. Ed. R. A. Hinde.
(Cambridge University Press.)

REFERENCES CHAPTER 9

R. B. Clark, (1960)
Habituation of the Polychaete *Nereis
pelagica* to Sudden Stimuli.
Animal Behaviour. **8**, 82–103.

M. P. Harris, (1971)
Species Separation in Gulls.
Modern Biology, selected readings, Ed.
R. Hoste. (Penguin.)

E. H. Hess, (1958)
Imprinting in Animals.
Scientific American. March, **198**.

J. Hirsch, R. H. Lindley,
E. C. Tolman, (1955)
An Experiment Test of an Alleged
Innate Sign Stimulus.
J. Comp. Physiol. Psychology. **48**,
278–280.

A. Lill, (1968)
An analysis of sexual isolation in the
domestic fowl.
Behaviour. **30**, (2, 3), 107–145.

R. Melzack, E. Penick, A. Beckett,
(1959)
The Problem of 'Innate Fear' of the
Hawk Shape; an Experimental Study
with Mallard Ducks.
J. Comp. Physiol. Psychology. **52**,
694–698.

T. C. Schneirla (1965) Aspects of
stimulus and organisation in
approach/withdrawal processes. *Adv.
Study Behaviour* **1**, 1–71.

REFERENCES CHAPTER 10

K. C. Montgomery, (1954)
The Role of the Exploratory Drive in
Learning.
J. Comp. Physiol. Psychology. **47**, 60–63.

J. Olds, P. Milner, (1954)
Positive Reinforcement Produced by
Electrical Stimulation of the Septal
Area and Other Regions of the Rat
Brain.
J. Comp. Physiol. Psychology. **47**,
419–427.

E. C. Tolman, C. H. Honzik, (1930)
Introduction and Removal of Reward
and Maze Performance in Rats.
Univ. Calif. Publ. Psychology. **4**,
257–275.

W. A. Van Bergeijk, (1971)
Anticipatory Feeding Behaviour in the
Bullfrog.
Modern Biology, selected readings. Ed.
R. Hoste. (Penguin Books.)

REFERENCES CHAPTER 11

M. S. Gazzaniga, (1967)
The Split Brain in Man.
Scientific American. August, **217**,
24–29.

H. Harlow, (1949)
The Formation of Learning Sets.
Psych. Rev. **56**, 51–65.

K. S. Lashley, (1926)
Studies of Cerebral Function in
Learning.
J. Comp. Neurol. 41.

D. Miyadi, (1964)
Social Life of Japanese Monkeys.
Science **143**, 783–786.

J. F. Shepard, (1933)
Higher Processes in the Behaviour of
Rats.
Proc. Nat. Acad. Sci. USA. **19**,
149–152.

REFERENCES CHAPTER 12

R. K. Andjus, F. Knopfelmacher,
R. W. Russell, A. Smith, (1958)
Effects of Hypothermia on Behaviour.
Nature. **176.4491**, 1015–1016.

J. Annett, (1973)
Programmed Learning.
New Horizons in Psychology. Ed.
Brian Foss (Penguin Books.)

S. H. Barondes, M. E. Jarvik, (1964)
The Influence of Actinomycin D on
Brain RNA Synthesis and on
Memory.
Journal of Neurochemistry. **11**.

S. H. Barondes, (1969)
The Recognition Molecules of the
Brain.
New Scientist. **41.635**, 278–280.

C. Blakemore, (1971)
Why We See What We See.
New Scientist. **51.769**, 614–617.

N. Chalmers, R. Crawley,
S. P. R. Rose, (1971)
The Biological Bases of Behaviour.
(Open University Press.) 1971.

J. R. Cooper, F. E. Bloom,
R. H. Roth, (1974)
*The Biological Basis of
Neuropharmacology.* 2nd Ed. (Oxford
University Press, Inc. New York.)

N. R. Ellis, D. K. Detterman,
D. Runcie, R. B. McCarver,
E. M. Craig, (1971)
Amnesic Effects in Short Term
Memory.
J. Exp. Psychol. **89**, 357–361.

D. H. Hubel, T. N. Wiesel, (1962)
Receptive Fields, Binocular
Interaction and Functional
Architecture in the Cat's Visual
Cortex.
J. Physiol. **160**, 106.

H. Hyden, E. Egyhazi, (1962)
Nuclear RNA Changes of Nerve Cells
During a Learning Experiment in
Rats.
Proc. Nat. Acad. Sci. USA. **48**,
1366–1373.

J. V. McConnell, (1962)
Memory Transfer Through
Cannibalism in Planarians.
J. Neuropsychiat. **3**, (suppl. 1) 542.

L. R. Peterson, M. J. Peterson, (1959)
Short Term Retention of Individual
Verbal Items.
J. Exp. Psychol. **58**, 193–198.

S. Sternberg, (1969)
Memory Scanning: Mental Processes
Revealed by Reaction Time
Experiments.
Amer. Sci. **57**, 421–457.

REFERENCES CHAPTER 13

I. Eibl-Eibesfeldt, (1961)
The Fighting Behaviour of Animals.
Scientific American. December, **205**.

V. H. Mark, F. R. Ervin, (1970)
Violence and the Brain. (Harper and
Row Inc. New York.)

D. D. Thiessen, (1972)
The Biology of Aggression; Evolution
and Physiology.
*Challenging Biological Problems –
Directions Towards their Solution.*
Ed. John A. Behnke. (Oxford
University Press New York.)

REFERENCES CHAPTER 14

D. Lack, (1965)
The Life of the Robin. (H. F. and G.
Witherby. 4th Ed.)

J. H. MacKintosh, (1970)
Territory Formation by Laboratory
Mice.
Animal Behaviour. **18**, 177–183.

N. Tinbergen, (1953)
Social Behaviour in Animals.
(Methuen.)

REFERENCES CHAPTER 15

J. B. Calhoun, (1962)
Population Density and Social
Pathology.
Scientific American. February, **206**.

P. Crowcroft, F. P. Rowe, (1958)
The Growth of Confined Colonies of
the Wild House Mouse, and the Effect
of Dispersal on Female Fecundity.
Proc. Zool. Soc. London. **131**, 357–365.

S. Milgram, (1963)
Behavioural Study of Obedience.
*Journal of Abnormal and Social
Psychology*. **67.4**, 371–378.

A. Payne, (1976)
Social Behaviour in Vertebrates.
(Heinemann Educational Books.)

T. Schjelderup-Ebbe, (1935)
Social Behaviour of Birds.
Handbook of Social Psychology.
947–972. (Clark University Press.)

REFERENCES CHAPTER 16

H. Esch, (1967)
The Evolution of Bee Language.
Scientific American. **216**, 97–104.

James L. Gould, (1975)
Honey Bee Recruitment. The
Dance-language Controversy.
Science. **189**, 685–693.

A. M. Wenner, (1964)
Sound Communication in Honey Bees.
Scientific American. April, **210**.

K. von Frisch, (1967)
*The Dance Language and Orientation
of Bees*. (Oxford University Press.)

REFERENCES CHAPTER 17

J. C. Coulson, (1966)
Influence of the Pair Bond and Age on
the Breeding Biology of the Kittiwake
Gull, *Rissa tridactyla*.
Journal of Animal Ecology. **35**,
269–279.

J. Huxley, (1914)
The Courtship of the Great Crested
Grebe.
Proc. Zool. Soc. London. **35**, (Reprinted
by Cape Editions 1968)

G. A. Parker, G. R. G. Hayhurst,
J. S. Bradley, (1974)
Attack and Defence Strategies in
Reproductive Interactions of *Locusta
migratoria*, and their Adaptive
Significance.
Z. Tierpsychol. **34**, 1–24.

V. C. Wynne-Edwards, (1962)
*Animal Dispersal in Relation to Social
Behaviour*. (Oliver and Boyd,
Edinburgh.)

REFERENCES CHAPTER 18

R. Dawkins, (1976)
The Selfish Gene. (Oxford University
Press.)

M. Impekoven, (1973)
The Response of Incubating
Laughing Gulls (*Larus atricilla*) to
Calls of Hatching Chicks.
Behaviour. **46**.

E. Noirot, (1972)
The Onset of Maternal Behaviour in
Rats, Hamsters and Mice.
Advances in the Study of Behaviour. **4**.

R. L. Trivers, (1974)
Parent-offspring Conflict
American Zoologist. **14.1**, 249–264.

REFERENCES CHAPTER 19

Jean Dorst, (1962)
The Migrations of Birds. (William
Heinemann.)

S. T. Emlen, (1975)
The Stellar Orientation System of a
Migratory Bird.
Scientific American. August, **233**.

D. R. Griffin, (1965)
Bird Migration. Science Study Series.
32. (Heinemann.)

R. J. Harrison, J. E. King, (1965)
Marine Mammals. (Hutchinson
University Library.)

G. Kramer, (1952)
Bird Orientation. *Ibis*. **94**, 265–285.

C. J. Krebs, J. H. Myers, (1974)
Population Cycles in Rodents.
Scientific American. June, **230**.

W. Rowan, (1927)
Migration and Reproductive Rhythm
in Birds.
Nature. **119.2882**, 351–352.

REFERENCES CHAPTER 20

A. Carr, (1965)
The Navigation of the Green Turtle.
Scientific American. May.

Jeremy Cherfas, (1977)
How Birds Follow Invisible Maps.
New Scientist. **75.1063**, 292–294.

G. V. T. Matthews, (1955)
Bird Navigation. (Cambridge University Press.)

C. Walcott, R. P. Green, (1974)
Orientation of Homing Pigeons Altered by a Change in the Direction of an Applied Magnetic Field.
Science. **184**.

REFERENCES CHAPTER 21

C. Limbaugh, (1961)
Cleaning Symbioses.
Scientific American. Aug., **205**.

REFERENCES CHAPTER 22

M. Bastock, A. Manning, (1955)
The Courtship of *Drosophila melanogaster.*
Behaviour. **8.(2,3)**, 85–111.

G. Beale, (1971)
Social Effects of Research in Human Genetics.
The Social Impact of Modern Biology. Ed. Watson Fuller. (Routledge and Kegan Paul.)

H. C. Bennet-Clark, A. W. Ewing, (1967) The Love Song of the Fruit Fly.
New Scientist. **36**, 230–232.

Gordon Claridge, S. Carter, W. I. Hume, (1973)
Personality Differences and Biological Variations; a Study of Twins.
International Series in Experimental Psychology. **18**. (Pergamon Press.)

K. Connolly, (1966)
The Genetics of Behaviour.
New Horizons in Psychology 1. 185–208. (Penguin Books.)

W. M. Court Brown, (1971)
The Study of Human Sex Chromosome Abnormalities with Particular Reference to Intelligence and Behaviour.
Modern Biology. Ed. R. Hoste. (Penguin Books.)

L. J. Eaves, J. L. Jinks, (1972)
Insignificance of Evidence for Differences in Heritability of IQ between Races and Social Classes.
Nature. **240.5375**, 84.

A. W. Griffiths, B. W. Richards, J. Zaremba, T. Ambramowicz, A. Stewart, (1970)
Psychological and Sociological Investigation of XYY Prisoners.
Nature. **227**, 290.

P. A. Jacobs, M. Brunton, M. M. Melville, R. D. Brittain, M. M. McClemont, (1965)
Aggressive Behaviour, Mental Subnormality and the XYY Male.
Nature. **208**, 1351.

A. Manning, (1961)
Effects of Artificial Selection for Mating Speed in *Drosophila melanogaster.*
Animal Behaviour. **9**, 82–92.

A. Mazur, L. Robertson, (1972)
Biology and Social Behaviour. (The Free Press. New York.)

J. Schwartz, (1976)
After Burt, What's Left?
New Scientist. **72.1026**, 330,

C. H. Southwick, (1970)
Genetic and Environmental Variables Influencing Animal Aggression.
Animal Aggression. 213–229 – Selected Readings Ed. Southwick. (Van Nostrand. Reinhold. Co. New York.)

S. G. Vandenberg, (1972)
The Future of Human Behaviour Genetics. *Genetics, Environment and Behaviour.* Eds. Ehrman, Omenn and Caspari. (Academic Press. N.Y.)

G. A. Van Oortmerssen, (1970)
Biological Significance, Genetics and Evolutionary Origin of Variability in Behaviour Within and Between Inbred Strains of Mice, *Mus musculus.*
Behaviour. **38**, 1–92.

REFERENCES CHAPTER 23

P. A. Johnsgard, (1965)
Handbook of Water-fowl Behaviour. (Cornell University Press.)

K. Lorenz, (1958)
The Evolution of Behaviour.
Scientific American. Dec., **199**.

Index